Behind these Doors:

Science Museum Makers

Behind these Doors:
Science Museum Makers

By MARGERY FACKLAM

ILLUSTRATED WITH PHOTOGRAPHS

Rand McNally & Company
Chicago   New York   San Francisco

Contents

Acknowledgments

THE AUTHOR is grateful for permission to use quotes from the following copyrighted materials: pages 23, 25, 29, bottom of page 33, and 37, from *Henry A. Ward, Museum Builder to America,* by Roswell Ward, 1948, by permission of the publisher, Rochester Historical Society, Rochester, N.Y., from volume XXIV of its publications; page 30, from *Adventurous Alliance* by Louise Hall Tharp, Copyright (c) 1959 by Louise Hall Tharp, by permission of the publisher, Little, Brown and Company, Boston, Mass.; page 32 and top of page 33, courtesy of the American Museum of Natural History from their Guide Leaflet, *The Story of Museum Groups;* pages 41–42, from *The Mounting of an Elephant Group* by Louis Jonas, and page 108, from *The Museum in America* by Laurence Vail Coleman, by permission of The American Association of Museums, Washington, D.C.; pages 50 and 50–51, from *Taxidermy and Zoological Collecting* by William T. Hornaday, 1916, by permission of the publisher, Charles Scribner's Sons, New York, N.Y.; pages 111, 117, and 123, from *Beyond Adventure* by Roy Chapman Andrews, Copyright (c) 1952, 1953, 1954 by Roy Chapman Andrews, by permission of the publisher, Duell, Sloan and Pearce, New York, N.Y.; page 125, from a paper, *A Naturalist in a University Museum,* by Dr. Alexander Ruthven, Ann Arbor, Mich., by permission of the author; pages 129 and 130, from the catalogue of the University of Iowa, Iowa City, Iowa, by permission of the university.

The author also acknowledges with thanks permission to reproduce the following photographs: pages 11 and 125, courtesy of the Smithsonian Institution; pages 19, 39, 41, 43, 45, 46, 56, 70, 91, 113, 114, 119, 122, and 126, courtesy of the American Museum of Natural History; pages 22, 27, 34, 40, 53, 99, and 100, courtesy of Ward's Natural Science Establishment, Inc.; pages 48, 49, 59, 82, 84, 90, 102, 103, 106, 128, and 132, courtesy of the Buffalo Museum of Science; pages 63 and 95, courtesy of the *Buffalo Courier Express* (photographs by Frank J. Schifferle); pages 78, 79, and 80, courtesy of the Los Angeles County Museum of Natural History (photographs by Mike Hatchimonji).

Illustrations

The Museum Makers 1

Two men scale a sheer cliff to tag a baby bald eagle; a small boy hesitantly touches a snake for the first time; a group of men and women gather at dawn to count migrating geese; an anthropologist launders a piece of Peruvian cloth forty-five hundred years old; a team of biologists mount underwater microphones to catch the sounds of the ocean's inhabitants; a taxidermist takes a limp skin and skillfully transforms it into a lifelike animal; a busload of schoolchildren stare at a herd of elephants.

These are the people who make natural history museums the busy places they are, full of the activity concerned with displaying and studying the living world.

One day you might explore the depths of the Indian Ocean or trudge the sands of the Gobi Desert, but for the many people who must take their adventure second-hand, a trip to a science museum is almost as fascinating and certainly more comfortable. High adventure to one man means scaling Mount Everest, and to another it means mounting the skeleton of a Brontosaurus. Museum work offers both possibilities.

At your first glance around the dimly lighted halls—staring back at silent stuffed animals, looking up at once-powerful dinosaurs that are now only outlines in bone—you may get the feeling that a natural history museum seems dead, a cemetery for things from the past. Natural history museums have been called "moth fodder" and "dead circuses" and even "menageries that don't eat."

But you need to be aware of more than the silence, more than the glass cases filled with objects. When you look behind the doors marked "Not Open to the Public" and into the rows of labeled storage cupboards, you begin to get an idea of the tremendous scope of the natural history museum. As you talk to the men and women who collect elephant skins and hummingbird eggs, diamonds and daisies, shrunken heads and arrowheads, you discover a group of people who make museums the extraordinary treasure-houses of the nation.

Today there are museums for almost everything (art, history, aviation, and circuses), and they range in size from a one-room frontier cabin to the Smithsonian Institution, a complex of buildings in Washington, D.C. In 1910 there were 600 registered museums listed by the American Association of Museums; in 1967 there were 4,598 museums of all kinds, and 1,500 of those had opened since 1950. The museum business is booming after a slow start.

Museums have been in business since the third cen-

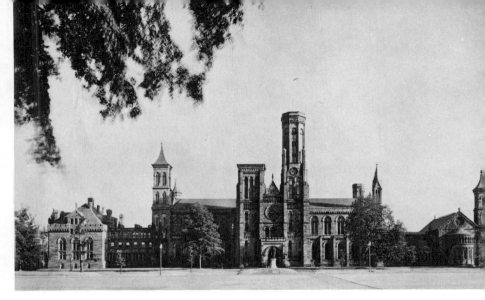

The original building of the Smithsonian Institution in Washington, D.C. Today there is a group of modern buildings.

tury before the birth of Christ, but they were as different from modern museums as a horse is from a car. The Ptolemaic kings of ancient Greece set aside part of the palace to house the library of Alexander the Great. It was a temple to the Muses—the nine goddesses of Greek mythology who inspired artists and scholars. This temple was called a *mouseion*. It was not open to the public, but was restricted to philosophers and wise men of the court who met for lectures and discussions. There was a small collection of art and manuscripts and possibly some natural history material. Aristotle was the first to take enough interest in natural history to describe and catalog some of it. The Greek mouseion was destroyed by fire in 48 B.C., and the word mouseion, or museum, wasn't used again for many centuries.

During the Middle Ages, when illiteracy was common, most of the scholars were churchmen, and the Christian churches functioned as museums to the extent that they were the source of knowledge and the exhibitors of great art treasures.

In the sixteenth century it became fashionable for princes and noble families to collect curios, stuffed animals, and freaks of nature, as well as paintings and sculpture. These collections were kept in rooms called *cabinets* in France and *museos* in Italy. Sometimes noble families combined their "daily exercise" with art when they displayed paintings in the long galleries of the cold stone castles. Even though the winter chill penetrated the thick walls, it was more comfortable to take an afternoon walk indoors than out.

The first natural history collection of importance in England was gathered by John Tradescant and his son, who were gardeners employed by the Duke of Buckingham and later by King Charles I. Mr. Tradescant had a catalog of his collection published in 1656 that included "12 cartloads of curiosities," including

> ... some kinds of birds, their eggs, beaks, feathers, claws, and spurs. Divers sorts of eggs, two feathers of the phoenix tail, Easter eggs of the patriarch of Jerusalem, the claw of the bird Rock who authors report is able to truss an elephant.

That collection was given to the city of Oxford. As men formed societies for the advancement of science, they usually started collections, too. The Royal Society of London did this in 1681.

The first great public collection in England, which became the British Museum, was started in 1753 by Sir Hans Sloane, the physician of Queen Anne. After Sir Hans's death, the collection was left to the government with the provisions that the public must be admitted free and that the government must provide a building for the collection. The government ran a lottery, selling 50,000 tickets with prizes from 10 to 10,000 pounds, to raise funds for the building.

But the British Museum could hardly have been called public as we think of it. Not more than sixty people were allowed in on one day, and then only in very small groups. A prospective visitor had to register at the porter's lodge four or five days in advance of his visit and list his name, "condition," and residence. This list was submitted to the museum's director, and, if he approved, he issued the tickets. A museum visit was not a spur-of-the-moment rainy-day activity.

Right from their inception American natural history museums differed from the Old World institutions. It was a new country and people were curious about such things as new plants, new animals, and the different Indian cultures; the aim of the museums was to show the people what they wanted to see.

The first museum to be opened in the American colonies was organized in 1773 by the Library Society of Charles-Town. These men, "taking into consideration the many Advantages and great Credit that would result," set out to collect materials that would provide a complete account of the natural history of the province of South Carolina. That museum is now the Charleston Museum.

In the 1750's Harvard students and professors collected unusual plant specimens, fossils, minerals, and animals and organized them in a "Repositerry of Curiosities." When that structure burned, a new "Museum" room became the start of the University Museum at Cambridge.

An artist in Philadelphia, Charles Willson Peale, turned a wing of his large home into an exhibition hall in 1814. At first he limited it to art, but added natural history later. His most popular exhibit was a collection of mammoth bones he had helped to excavate and assemble. Peale distributed tickets which said:

> The Birds and the Bees will teach thee! Admit the Bearer to Peale's Museum, containing the wonderful works of NATURE and the curious works of ART.

An Englishman, who had never been to America and knew no Americans, died in 1829. His will, bequeathing his entire estate to his nephew, Henry James Hungerford, stated that if his nephew died without having left a child, his fortune, amounting to almost $550,-000, should be used to set up "at Washington, under the name of the Smithsonian Institution, an establishment for the increase and diffusion of Knowledge among men." James Smithson had been a trustee of the British Museum and a chemist and mineralogist. Some historians think that his strange bequest was Smithson's revenge against the British Museum for turning down a scientific paper he had written. Whatever his reasons, Smithson's will caused disturbance in the Congress of the United States over the precise use of the bequest. Finally, in 1846, the Smithsonian Institution was established by an act of Congress.

Although nothing had been mentioned in the will about a museum, the Institution quickly became the "nation's attic," as people sent in things listed in records as "A Book from Siam, said to be a very interesting novel, received from a fashionable young lady," and a "Series of domestic Turkey feather dusters, 5 sizes." The first director of the Smithsonian, Joseph Henry, made eloquent pleas for a museumless Smithsonian. His interpretation of an institution for the increase and diffusion of knowledge among men meant the sending out of expeditions, the sponsoring of research, the writing of scientific papers, and the distribution of thousands of pamphlets. His quick rejoinder to people who reminded him that expeditions brought back many objects was that such items could be distributed to museums in other cities. But it was a losing battle for Mr. Henry as the collections grew and grew.

Now the Smithsonian Institution consists of thirteen divisions, including the United States National Museum, made up of the Museum of Natural History and the Museum of History and Technology. The Institution includes the National Zoological Park, the International

Exchange Service, the National Gallery of Art, the National Collection of Fine Arts, the Freer Gallery of Art, the National Portrait Gallery, the National Air and Space Museum, the John F. Kennedy Center for the Performing Arts, the Radiation Biology Laboratory, the Science Information Exchange, the Smithsonian Astrophysical Observatory, and the tropical research institute known as the Canal Zone Biological Area.

The Smithsonian staff sends millions of publications out each year. They answer about 65,000 requests for information, care for approximately 3,000 zoo animals, and have responsibility for more than 60 million items worth a billion dollars. Probably few of the 18 million visitors a year realize that somewhere in the maze of halls and storage rooms there are 13 million fossils and 16 million insects. James Smithson probably never dreamed that his money and one sentence in his will would breed such a remarkable place.

In 1841 Scudder's American Museum opened in New York City under the management of Phineas Taylor Barnum. He made a fortune charging admission and bringing entertainment to the public in a time when movies and television did not exist. He exhibited a midget he called Tom Thumb and an elderly Negro woman said to have been George Washington's nurse. He had a genius for showmanship, but not for science.

At the same time another man, Louis Agassiz, a scientist from Switzerland teaching in America, was doing for science what Barnum did for oddities. Agassiz was the kind of man who today would most likely have a television series on glaciers or fossil fishes. He popularized natural history with dynamic public lectures. The halls in which he spoke usually were so crowded that there was standing room only, and Agassiz used every opportunity to press home his point that museums are a great means of education and research. He liked to urge people to study nature, not books.

Agassiz was born in a small village in Switzerland in 1807. As a teen-ager he went to Zurich because his father wanted him to study medicine, but he found natural science much more interesting. He couldn't afford to buy books, so he copied them in longhand on any bits and scraps of paper he could find and stitched them together with thread. There were few regularly scheduled classes in European universities at that time, and a student was expected to learn enough, in any way he could, to pass the examinations. When Agassiz came to America he was horrified at the spoon-fed education dished out by Harvard, which he called a glorified high school. His lectures and research did much to change that.

Agassiz became an authority on fossil fish, and he presented the theory of the movement of glaciers. In the early 1800's all geological markings were thought to be left by the flood that took place in Noah's time. Agassiz observed the movements of ice masses and huge scratches and paths of boulders through the Alps. He traveled in Europe and eventually put together the astounding theory of an age of ice. Many scientists denounced him. Even his friend and benefactor, the great scientist Baron von Humboldt, begged him not to make a fool of himself with such wild ideas.

Strangely enough, years later, when Agassiz had become head of the important Museum of Comparative Zoology at Harvard, he, in turn, would not accept another man's new theory. Agassiz sided with those who accepted the traditional ideas of spontaneous creation against Darwin's theory of evolution. He believed that all the fossils he studied did not support the idea of change. Many of his students left him because of their different opinions, but none of them ever ceased to be influenced by this man's enthusiasm for the natural world and the building of museums for the study of it.

Some of Agassiz' students went on to build museums. Frederic Ward Putnam, known as the Father of American Archeology, was on leave as Director of the Peabody Museum of Archeology at Harvard when he helped with the formation of Chicago's Field Museum of Natural History. Albert Smith Bickmore, one of Agassiz' first students, conceived the idea for the American Museum of Natural History in New York City and became its first director. The American Museum, now the largest natural history museum in the world, was a radical change from other museums because it was incorporated by businessmen instead of by scientists and professors. Bickmore made it a truly public museum by presenting lecture series and programs to which the people responded with astonishing speed. The teaching of natural history had grown in importance.

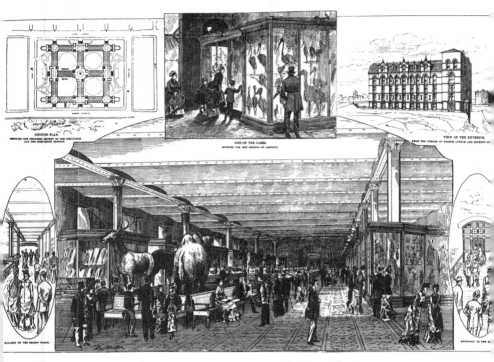

The opening of the American Museum of Natural History was publicized with these sketches in the Daily Graphic *on December 22, 1877.*

The original taxidermy shop at Ward's had animals in all stages of preparation. The men in the center are building the armature of a rhinoceros with wooden strips.

building in Rochester. Henry Ward was in business, and he found that speculating in natural history paid.

When he was introduced to the widow of the founder of the Cliquot wine industry, Ward requested permission to visit the vast caverns of Paris limestone that were her wine cellars. She expected Ward to putter around and bring out a pocketful of fossils. Instead he arrived with a crew of peasants and they mined two tons of specimens.

Ward tracked down specimens as though he were Noah urgently saving samples before the earth disappeared. He filled notebooks with lists of the "wants" of museum curators, and most of the time he was able to supply them. He went from Moscow, where he saw the remains of the Great Siberian Mammoth that had been frozen in a riverbed, to the Nile, where he crawled deep into the pits filled with mummified crocodiles sacrificed centuries earlier to the river gods. He shipped to Rochester boatloads of skinned camels, gorillas, snakes, boxes of fossils, and tons of minerals.

He added another item to his growing list of supplies, and he described it in a letter:

> Whenever I have found anything (fossil) of peculiar interest, I have attained a cast of it. The result is, that with the very large stores which I had before, I can now offer to American savants and institutions faithful copies of almost every noted fossil in the noted European cabinets. I hope to issue an illustrated catalogue of these casts, got up upon a reasonable scientific plan. I shall be able to offer over 500 casts from every animal kingdom.

This meant that small museums without the money to send expeditions out would be able to exhibit exact copies of huge fossils, most famous of which was the giant ground sloth, the *Megatherium cuvieri*, that stood seven feet high and almost eighteen feet long. In Ward's first catalog, published in 1866, it was described thus:

> This gigantic fossil was first made known to the scientific world in 1789. It was discovered on the banks of River Luxan, near the city of Buenos Ayres, and was subsequently transmitted to Madrid, where, for half a century, it excited the most lively speculations among all European naturalists, who were so fortunate as to see it.

The model of this sloth was made of 124 different

casts representing 175 bones. It was sold, in 1874, for
$800 because, in Ward's words, it was "a tedious and
absorbing task which occupied the writer and two assistants for a period of nearly two months." To make the
price more reasonable for small museums, Ward offered
the model in a do-it-yourself kit, unpainted and unas-
sembled, for $250. An added note in the catalog offered
to send men to assemble the sloth if the museum paid
the men's expenses.

As Ward's Natural Science Establishment grew, the
museums of the nation grew. Ward was a public relations man in a time when promotional jobs had no title.
He spent as much time trying to arouse citizens to start
museums in their cities as he did on collecting trips.
Ward believed so strongly in public museums that he
promoted them by extreme methods. Sometimes he
transported a huge collection, including the cast of the
Megatherium, to a city for a temporary display. This
involved days of packing, uncertain shipping by jostling
railways or horse-drawn wagons, and the task of setting
the exhibit in place. Then Ward called on prominent
people to encourage interest in a public subscription to
pay for the collection as a basis for a museum.

In central New York State, about this time, another
man decided to capitalize on the public's interest in fossils and inadvertently created a boom for Ward's Establishment. The Onondaga Giant occupied newspapers'
front pages for days, and fossils became a topic of con-
versation. This so-called giant was a hoax, an immense

"petrified man" supposedly found buried near Onondaga, New York. Ward saw it as a fake and wrote:

> The Onondaga Giant is the work of a sculptor, cut out of a single block of the gypseous limestone which forms large beds in this vicinity.

Nevertheless, people were intrigued and traveled for miles to pay to see the monster. This interest was reflected in the increase in orders Ward suddenly received for fossils and their casts.

By now Ward was shipping tons of material. He added plant and insect specimens and anatomical charts made in Paris. He stocked glass models of invertebrates intricately made by the Blaschka family, expert glass-blowers from Europe, who had been brought to the United States to prepare an entire collection of lifelike glass flowers for Harvard University, where they are still on display.

The people of Rochester never tired of watching the strange shipments that arrived by barge on the Erie Canal to be loaded into horse-drawn carts that would take them to Ward's Establishment. Sometimes a wagon would lumber by carrying a giant meteor or a mound of boxes marked in strange languages. Often on a hot summer day a strong smell would precede the wagon, and then people knew it might carry a load of monkey skins and bones from South America or a polar-bear carcass from the Arctic.

Ward had suppliers in many parts of the world.

Small boys living near Ward's shop sold him snakes, turtles, birds, and bird eggs—a wonderful way to earn pocket money. Amateur collectors wrote for a list of Ward's wants and sent him everything from worms to wombats.

The Vassar Female Academy ordered from Ward a "complete geological cabinet not to exceed $8,000," and later ordered a zoological collection. Included in the second order was a huge mounted gorilla that caused a commotion because prudent people, conscious of the new talk of evolution, thought the animal looked too much like a misshapen man. For many years the gorilla stood at Vassar wearing a pair of modest shorts.

Exposition fever took hold of America in the late 1800's, and it was the greatest thing that ever happened for museums. Almost every city that held an exposition was left with the embryo of a museum, and people went home from expositions anxious for their city to have a museum.

In 1875 Henry Ward went to the Chicago Exposition, at the invitation of Fredric Putnam, with an immense exhibit including the Megatherium, great blocks of quartz crystals, dozens of mounted animals, and reproductions of the crown jewels of Europe that dazzled visitors. As background for many of the skeleton casts, Ward had frightening life-size drawings of prehistoric monsters. Children stood wide-eyed and stunned before the ancient animals. Teachers, caught in the center of the evolution debates, took notes. Women loved the stuffed birds of paradise and ostriches that would make such elegant hats. Farmers, miners, businessmen—all

At the 1893 World's Fair in Chicago, Henry Ward, wearing his high gray hat, exhibited his most dramatic skeletons.

were having their first look at the things they had only read about before. And Henry Ward ambled around his display wearing a high gray hat so anyone wanting to purchase his collection could be told to "look for the man in the high gray hat." Most of the exhibit was sold to the Chicago Academy of Science, and it, with other exhibits from the fair, formed the nucleus of Chicago's Field Museum of Natural History.

Ward supplied Washington and Lee University and the universities of Virginia, Milwaukee, and Syracuse. In 1876 Philadelphia held an International Centennial Exposition that brought the latest scientific and technical ideas to the American people. Imagine what it must have been like for visitors to be able to see an exposition in those days, when there were none of the quick means of communication we have today to bring people the latest reports on science. They saw powerful guns and railroad equipment from the German Krupp works; they saw a Russian exhibit of state vocational training. The Corliss engine was there, and the "electrical talking machine" of Dr. Bell. But the buildings weren't filled, and the officials of the fair asked Henry Ward to bring an exhibit.

He took a reproduction of the giant mammoth he had seen earlier in Siberia. At the Royal Institute of Stuttgart two men had built a model of the mammoth from wood, covered it with wire, cloth, papier-mâché, and finally with hair made from Indian palm fiber. The tusks were made from wood and the trunk of cardboard. It stood 16 feet tall and 26 feet long. When Ward bought it he worked with a group of mechanics for three weeks to take it apart and pack it in 14 crates. The ocean freight cost $981. From New York it had to be loaded on barges and taken to Rochester on the Erie Canal. There was great publicity, and newspapers carried exaggerated drawings of prehistoric monsters.

After that Ward couldn't send out catalogs fast enough. He went on to the Pittsburgh Industrial Exposition where he showed a giraffe, a buffalo, a polar bear, an anteater, a seal, monkeys, lions, a manatee, a kangaroo, an alligator, a shark, an iguana, and the famous mammoth. The preparators at his shop were very busy keeping up with orders for these mounted animals.

Ward sold a $20,000 collection of skeletons, fossils, and mounted animals to San Francisco, which was later purchased by the California Academy of Science. Mark Hopkins gave a million dollars for a building for this collection and funds to add to the exhibit.

Another museum was planned in California. This time the owners of a resort development in San Diego at the Coronado Beach Hotel wanted to attract a "high class of people." They thought perhaps a museum would add the right touch of culture. They set aside $40,000 and ordered an exhibit of marine life because the hotel faced the ocean. Ward outdid himself with a whale skeleton, a life-size model of a giant squid, and an octopus. Then he designed an innovation which he called "the polyzoopticon." He described it as "an enormous circular stage, revolving by clockwork, divided into five compartments by canvas screens which converge at the center." Each section represented a different zone of the earth and its animal life: one was the Arctic zone done in realistic snow; the second was a scene of North American animals; and the third showed a landslide in the Alps with animals being crushed beneath falling rocks. The fourth scene was a desert with a hyena gnawing bones and a vulture overhead, and the last section showed the jungle with a large boa constrictor and alligators crawling through thick vegetation. Ward knew that drama attracted people, and that if you didn't get people to look they could not learn. It took sixteen railroad cars to carry the equipment to San Diego where Ward and several assistants assembled it.

Ward, ever on the lookout for specimens, was at the Fulton Fish Market in New York City one day when he spotted a new variety of eel. He purchased some of the small slippery creatures and decided to carry them in his closed umbrella with a string around the top. He got on a Broadway bus, leaned back, and dozed. Feeling something strange on his feet, he looked down to see eels escaping. He knew he couldn't capture all of them without attracting considerable attention. Very calmly he got off the bus. Blocks away he could hear women screaming: "Snakes! snakes!"

The business of making museums is indeed unusual. It requires the dedication of men and women who would agree with Louis Agassiz when he wrote, in 1870:

> Nowadays a museum is no longer a collection of curiosities. It is an apparatus as indispensable for the progress of modern civilization as a chemical laboratory. A museum should be open to all and furnish to all the information required.

Early Taxidermy 3

Whenever a group of museum-goers follows a guide past the lifelike animal exhibits one of the questions invariably asked is, "Is it real, is it stuffed?" This is a compliment to the realism achieved by the taxidermists.

Taxidermy is the art of preserving skin, fur, feathers, or scales. The word comes from two Greek words, *taxis*, meaning arrangement or preparation, and *derma*, meaning skin. Prehistoric man tanned animal skins for clothing. Ancient Egyptians practiced a kind of taxidermy when they embalmed dogs, cats, and crocodiles to put in tombs. American Indians preserved heads of porcupines and loons for decoration.

But the first taxidermy for display, as far as anyone can discover, was done on a group of birds killed in India 350 years ago and taken to Holland where they were arranged on perches with wire. The oldest specimen of a mounted mammal is a rhinoceros in the Royal Museum of Vertebrates in Florence, Italy, also prepared in the 1600's.

The first forms of taxidermy were literally stuffing, with the animal suspended head down and rammed full of straw. It is impossible to achieve a natural pose in an animal that looks nothing like its original form. The evolution of taxidermy brought with it an attempt at realism in the backgrounds, too.

Not all people agreed with such fancy notions as popularizing displays of birds with outstretched wings or animals running through real leaves and moss.

One interested professor wrote in 1874:

> Spread eagle styles of mounting, artificial rocks, and flowers are entirely out of place in a collection of any scientific pretensions or designed for public instruction. Besides, they take up too much room. Artistic grouping of an extensive collection is usually out of the question; and when this is unattainable, half-way efforts in that direction should be abandoned in favor of severe simplicity. Birds look best, on the whole, in uniform rows, assorted according to size, as far as a natural classification allows.

Fortunately most curators were aware of the fact that you cannot teach a visitor unless you can interest him. If he doesn't want to know what the animal is, he won't stop to read the label. Sir William Henry Flower, director of the British Museum from 1884 to 1898, began to change the character of his exhibits and display animals in lifelike groups. A private collector in England, E. T. Booth, wrote of his bird collection:

> The chief object has been to endeavor to represent the birds in situations somewhat similar to those in which they were obtained.

Many preparators felt that the art of taxidermy would never allow more realism, but there are people in every business and in every age who think their field has gone as far as it can. When the next step in taxidermy came along—the covering of a manikin with the specimen's skin instead of stuffing it—one taxidermist wrote pessimistically:

> The attempts that have been made to represent animals by this artificial method have been very limited, and have proved in most instances unsuccessful. The general form may indeed be closely imitated, but as the larger classes are covered either with hair, feathers, or scales, substances which from their very nature defy the utmost ingenuity of man to imitate, it is more than probable this art will never make any considerable progress, at least so far as regards the great majority of animals.

That taxidermist did not reckon with men like Carl Akeley or Frederick Lucas, or all the other men trained by Ward, or with modern preparators. What a surprise he would have if he were to walk into any museum today. Man has, indeed, imitated nature successfully.

One day a letter came for Henry Ward from a young man at Iowa State Agricultural College. It said:

> I wish to ask in the first place if there is any chance of learning (taxidermy) in your establishment. I have considerable knowledge of mounting birds and stuffed many specimens for the college museum last year. But my knowledge of art is limited and it is my wish and determination to make a first-class taxidermist. What can you do for me?
>
> Respectfully yours,
> W. T. Hornaday

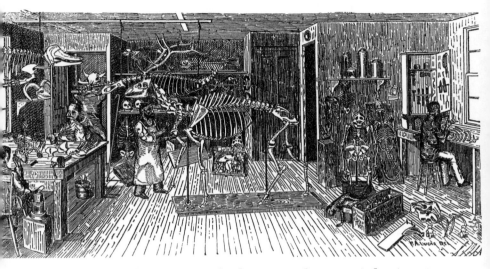

Frederick A. Lucas, who became a director of the American Museum, made this sketch of the laboratory in which skeletons were mounted at Ward's, where he started his career.

Hornaday went to Ward's Establishment and became not only an expert taxidermist, but an outstanding naturalist. In 1879 he exhibited, for Ward's, a group of orangutans at the meeting of the American Association for the Advancement of Science, which had been established in 1848. The orangutan mount was one of the first natural groupings, now called habitat groups, and it influenced museum techniques strongly. When other taxidermists saw the dramatic effect, they went back to their shops with new ideas. Robert Colgate, one of the group of men who incorporated the American Museum of Natural History, bought the orangutans for that museum.

Hornaday organized the National Society of American Taxidermists to raise the standards of taxidermy and to educate the public so that they would know the difference between scientific taxidermy and the stuffed animals that were popular in people's parlors at that time. He is especially remembered for instigating laws to save the American bison from extinction, and for his work at the American Museum of Natural History.

Captain Lucas, a sea captain who had a seventeen-year-old son, wrote to ask Ward what on earth to do with a boy "only good enough to skin snakes."

Ward's answer was, "Send him on."

So Frederick Lucas joined Ward's Establishment and was put to work on an order that Louis Agassiz had placed for some skeletons. Lucas' first job was to cut up a domestic pig, but the man who was in charge of the osteology lab (the skeleton department) so jealously guarded his methods that he didn't want a helper. Ward, therefore, put Lucas at other work until he learned every step of the business. The climax of Lucas' career was the directorship of the American Museum.

The list of Ward alumni is an impressive list of men who became artists, zoo directors, museum curators, aquarium managers, preparators in the largest museums, and professors of zoology, geology, and botany at the best universities.

try, mourned the loss of Jumbo, but he was also anxious to preserve what he could of his greatest attraction. He called his friend Henry Ward, who went immediately to St. Thomas with Carl Akeley, then twenty-two, and another taxidermist. By the time the men got to Jumbo the animal had lain in the hot sun beside the wrecked train for a day and a half. Akeley reported to friends later that it was, literally, a stinking job.

First they carefully measured Jumbo and recorded all the data. Then, with the help of six butchers from surrounding small towns, they skinned the elephant. The thick, bristly hide, weighing 1,538 pounds, was loaded into a huge wooden tank of saltwater mixed with alum, and the whole thing was shipped to Rochester to be tanned. After the butchers cut as much flesh from the bones as possible, the skeleton was packed into boxes that filled half a boxcar. Jumbo's heart, eyes, stomach, and the rest of the viscera were sent along with the bones. There was no refrigeration, and a newspaper report from Rochester told readers that the shipment made "quite an odoriferous as well as visual spectacle for the people of Rochester."

The accident occurred near the end of September, and Barnum wanted the elephant mounted and ready to roll with the circus train by March when the spring circus season opened. Ward had a special building put up for Akeley to use in mounting the skin, and he had a brick tank constructed for Akeley to use for macerating (decomposing the flesh from the bones) the skeleton. Akeley's biggest problem was to build an animal

*Carl Akeley built a manikin of Jumbo of planks
and oak crosspieces fastened together with iron
plates. Over this skeleton he fastened narrow
strips of basswood steamed to bend easily.*

that would last through the railroad travel and rain-
storms.

First Akeley built a wooden manikin, following as
exactly as he could the dimensions of the live Jumbo.
After the skin was cured, scraped, and poisoned with
arsenic to prevent decay, Akeley stretched it over the
manikin. Because, as Akeley said, "It always rains on
circus day," he nailed the skin to the wooden form with

thousands of countersunk nails to prevent shrinkage.

The skeleton presented a new set of problems. The skull had been shattered by the train, but all the pieces had been saved. Using a wooden framework, glue, and lots of papier-mâché, Akeley reconstructed the skull. The completed Jumbo was an impressive sight, standing twelve feet tall. He was delivered March 4 in a gay wagon the circus had designed specially for him.

This stiff Jumbo does not compare with today's work, but it set a new standard for large animal taxidermy. After the stuffed Jumbo traveled with the circus for many years, it was given to Tufts University in Medford, Mass. The skeleton was given to the American Museum.

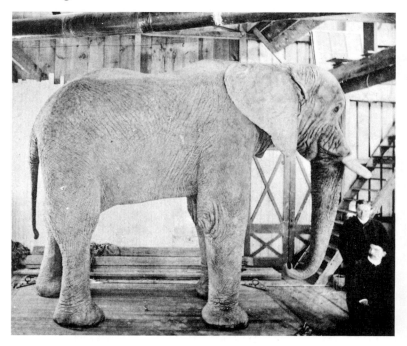

An elephant skin is swept and cleaned before it is mounted on a manikin.

The building of an elephant is one of the most dramatic things a taxidermist ever gets to do. It is a job that takes much planning and much ingenuity. There is no detailed manual for building elephants, and every preparator adds his own innovations as he works.

One of the taxidermists who worked on the elephants shown in the photographs on pages 43, 45, and 46 expressed the excitement he felt at being part of the re-creation of a specimen. He said:

> The feeling of life in that great bulk, the power of those marvelous legs, the sensitiveness of the trunk, the head full of countless expressive detail, and those marvelous eyes that speak of gentleness; to be able to

bring back in the elephant such lifelike naturalness is true art.

The method most widely used is the one devised by Carl Akeley, and that is the method described here. Earlier taxidermists believed that the skin had to fit the form. If the skin was too small, the form was shaved down a bit. If the skin was too large, they put in a few more wrinkles here and there. Akeley's method required great artistry and great accuracy, but it resulted in a perfect and lifelike image of the animal.

The first step is to obtain the animal. Children on museum tours look up into the soft eyes of a mounted bear or elephant and ask the guide, "Did they have to shoot him?" And the guide always wishes she didn't have to say "Yes." But, of course, the shooting of one specimen by one museum for generations of people to see is much more reasonable than the shooting of hundreds of elephants by hunters who merely want trophies for their walls or who shoot for the excitement of the hunt.

As soon as the animal is killed in the field, or when it dies in the zoo, the taxidermist measures it accurately and records as much detail of the appearance and size as he can. He makes precise notes on the coloring and on the surrounding area in which the animal lived. If possible he also takes movies of live animals so he can study muscle movements and posture later.

Back in his studio he makes a scale model, a miniature of the group to be on display. When this is satis-

Above: The big bull in the Indian elephant group at the American Museum of Natural History in one of the first stages of preparation. The wooden framework is being rounded out and shaped with screening.

Below: After tons of clay are modeled over the armature to build an exact duplicate of the elephant, the wet skin is worked into place.

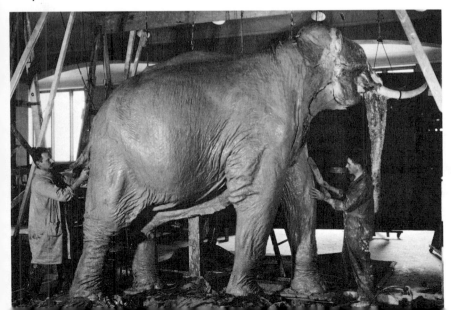

factory, he begins the life-size mount by building an armature which is the skeleton of a sculpture.

The armature for an elephant is a frame made from flat pieces of wood shaped in the outline of the backbone, breast, and belly of the animal. It is made in two halves so the elephant can be split open at a later stage. A wire cloth (screening) is nailed to these frames and is supported from the inside by braces shaped to give roundness to the body. The leg bones are put in place as the armatures for the model legs, and the real skull is used as the basis for the head. The completed armature is a monster shell of wire cloth and plaster held up by trusses, overhead beams, and cable wires. The entire thing is shellacked, and tons of potters clay is modeled over it.

The modeling of the clay is the most important step because the clay sculpture will be the shape of the finished animal. The preparator is a sculptor without a live model, so he must constantly check his work against the field measurements and notes. Once in a while he tries the skin on the form. When the model is completed it is covered with a thin clay composition that will act as an adhesive for the skin.

The clumsy, lifeless skin is then hauled over the clay monster and patiently and firmly pulled, pushed, and worked into place. It may take weeks of this tiring work before the skin begins to regain its original shape and liveliness. During this time it is kept covered with wet blankets. Sometimes the team of taxidermists work-

Plaster covers the skin of the modeled elephant. After it dries, the clay is scooped out and replaced by a light layer of papier-mâché. When the plaster is removed, a shell of hard skin, reinforced from inside, is left.

The head is being joined to the body. A hole is left in the belly through which a man can climb to fasten the head on from the inside.

ing on the project take turns sleeping in the lab in order
to be there to keep the skin moist.

With the skin in place the elephant may look finished, but it is not. The tons of clay under the skin make
the animal much too heavy to be practical. Mounted
specimens must be as strong as possible with the least
possible weight so they can be moved.

Carl Akeley devised the method for removing all
the clay, leaving a shell of skin. He oiled the skin and
coated it with plaster. When this coat of plaster is completely dry and supported by any necessary braces, the
elephant is split in half. The armature, you will remem-
ber, was built in two pieces. All the clay from the inside
is scooped out and replaced by a layer of plaster. At this
point the skin has a coat of plaster inside and out. This
is allowed to dry for about a month.

By the time it has dried thoroughly the skin has set
into a permanent shape. Now the inside coat of plaster
is carefully taken out. The inside of the skin is vacuumed
and shellacked. Then it is backed up with several layers
of papier-mâché and screening. The result is a durable,
strong, and very light inner shell. It is doubly secured
by adding wooden ribs much like the ribs of a canoe that
add rigidity.

Now the outer jacket is broken away from the skin.
The plaster falls away easily because the skin has shrunk
a bit in drying and because the skin had been oiled.

The ears and tail, which were made in separate
molds, are put in place. The temporary tusks, which were
made of plaster, are removed and the real tusks, which

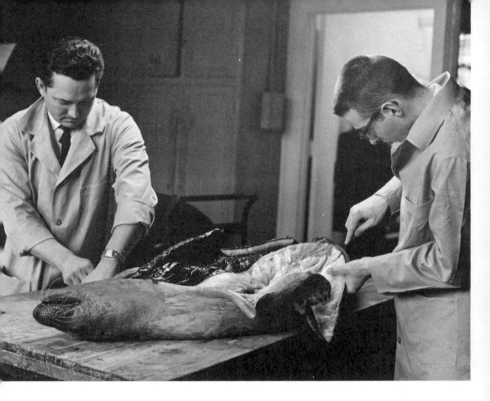

Above: A sea lion that died at the zoo is skinned as the first step in preparing a mount. Below, left: The taxidermist has made a papier-mâché model, using the measurements of the sea lion. Below, right: The tanned skin of the sea lion is glued into place.

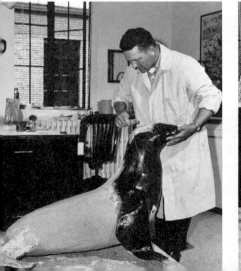
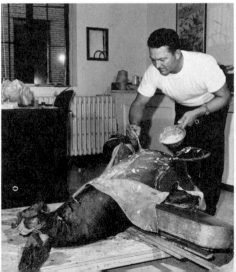

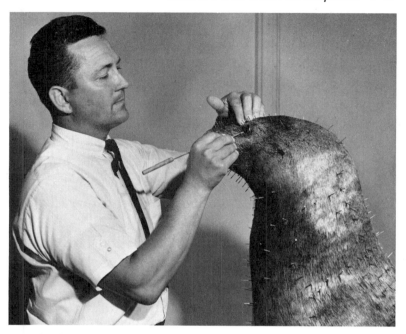

Hundreds of nails hold the sea lion's skin in place until it has dried completely. Glass or plastic eyes are put in to give a final realistic touch.

had been stored in a protective wax coating, are put in place. The two halves are fastened together, leaving a manhole in the belly of the elephant so the preparators can crawl inside to fasten the head. Glass or plastic eyes are placed under the four-inch eye lashes.

The last steps include dusting, vacuuming, and cleaning with wire brushes, as well as a final cleaning with a mixture of neat's-foot oil and benzine. The mounted elephant may have occupied the taxidermists for one or two years.

How Do You Make a Skeleton?

Man is ever intrigued by his own insides. A skeleton seems to draw people to it whether it is in a classroom, a Halloween display, or a museum.

Skeletons are used in the study of comparative anatomy, bone diseases, growth, and evolution. Art schools buy skeletons because artists must study anatomy in order to sketch accurate figures.

Because so many human skeletons are used in high school biology classrooms, medical schools, and museums, people imagine they must be plastic reproductions. But according to one of the leading biological supply houses, it is as expensive to make a good plastic reproduction as it is to assemble the real thing. And in order to study the minute variations in bones, schools prefer authentic skeletons.

The men and women who work with bones are called osteologists, and they work in osteology laboratories equipped with things as various as dentists' drills, block and tackle pulleys suspended from the ceiling, small beetles, and strong acids.

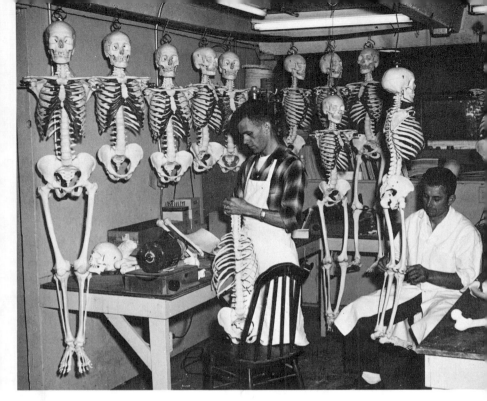

The human skeleton assembly line in a commercial supply house.

Human skeletons are sent to America from India where, because of religious beliefs different from those of the western world, bodies do not necessarily have to be buried. Indian hospitals sterilize and package bones for shipment to suppliers in all parts of the world.

At the biological supply houses the bones are bleached, sorted, and carefully assembled. Many of the teeth must be replaced by artificial ones because of extensive decay. Sometimes the osteologists find deformities or signs of unusual development in the skulls which are of special value for study.

The first step in preparing a skeleton is always the same, but the methods of completion vary with the preparator.

The curator of a zoo may call the director of a museum some morning with the message, "We have a dead zebra for you." When the animal is delivered at the museum it is carefully skinned with a sharp knife. The skin is either sent to a tannery or tanned at the museum if equipment is available. Special care is taken with the skin because its condition will determine the appearance of the mounted animal.

Next the animal is "roughed out." This means that most of the flesh is cut away, leaving the bony framework as intact as possible. A roughed-out skeleton can be dried and stored for many years before it is made into an attractive skeleton by relaxing it in fresh water and then cleaning, bleaching, and mounting it.

Commercial supply houses that receive hundreds of orders for skeletons must use an assembly (or rather a disassembly) line method to turn out finished mounts quickly. After the roughing out, the bones are cleaned of remaining flesh with a chisel-edged bone scraper, leaving the connecting tissue at each joint. The skeleton is kept wet throughout this procedure. It is placed in a bath of ammonia and water for several days in order to soak the blood from the bones.

After this soaking step, the skeleton is rinsed in clear water and scrubbed with chlorine bleach. The bones are rinsed again in clear water and then soaked in a container of hydrogen peroxide and water for twenty-four hours. The skeleton is taken out and dried after this last bleaching. The final step before mounting is degreasing by placing the bones in carbon tetrachloride. If the skeleton is that of a large animal such as the zebra, tiny holes would be drilled in the long bones to allow the grease to be removed more freely.

Many museums use a "bug room." This takes longer, but museums are not in a hurry. You know you are approaching the bug room before you see it. The sweet musty smell of decay reaches beyond the thick metal door, but it is an odor you forget as you work in the midst of it.

After the skeleton is roughed out and dried so it will not become moldy, it is placed on shelves where *Dermestes vulpinus*—a black beetle about as large as your little fingernail—can eat the tissue. This beetle lays eggs which hatch into white worms, called larvae, and these larvae are the real workers.

It is possible for the Dermestes larvae to clean the bones of a moose, a bear, an ostrich, a wolf, and several fish and reptiles in one room in three days. The advantage of bone cleaning by the bug method is its gradualness. The bones can be checked frequently and removed when the beetles have eaten away most of the tissue. Any remaining bits of tissue can be picked or brushed away. The bones are then bleached, degreased, and dried.

Finally, each bone, no matter how tiny, is numbered with indelible ink, and the bones are dipped, sprayed, or painted with a plastic coating as a preservative.

Mounting skeletons is a craft requiring great skill and patience, and every field has its expert. Samuel Harmsted Chubb, of the staff of the American Museum of Natural History, was such an expert. He started his career about as early as it's possible to start by collecting skeletons when he was seven years old. He combed the

Samuel Chubb at work on a skeleton attached to his original scaffold. The suspending cords had small weights on the ends which allowed free movement of parts and eliminated the use of knots.

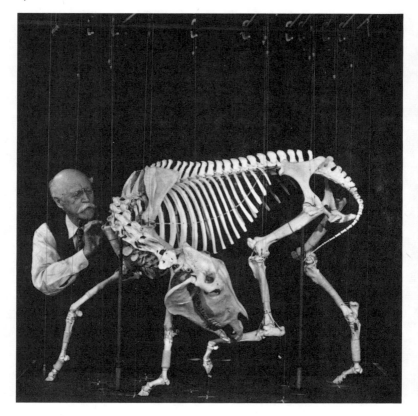

fields and woods for decaying animals around his home in Palenville, New York. He soon learned that if he marked the spot and let the carcass alone for a while, when he returned the flesh would be cleaned off by scavengers and larvae of insects—nature's bug-room method. He had a particularly fine collection of horse skulls, and one day he arranged a startling show for his father, who was a country doctor.

Chubb fastened the lower jaws of the horse skulls firmly to the edge of a shed roof. He attached the skulls to the lower jaws with large hinges, and poked long sticks through the *foramen magnum* (the hole at the base of the skull). To each stick he attached a long string. Chubb waited behind the shed until dusk when his father drove his horse and buggy into the yard. Then he yanked the strings, gnashing the teeth of the ghostly puppets, scaring the wits out of the live horse.

By the time he was sixteen, Samuel Chubb had become a machinist, spending all his spare hours at the American Museum of Natural History. He continued to mount skeletons at home. One day, feeling courageous, he pointed out to the curator of the department of vertebrate paleontology that the skeletons were mounted wrong. No doubt the curator was astounded, but he realized that the boy spoke seriously after he examined a cat skeleton Chubb had mounted. The curator bought the cat for forty dollars and ordered the skeletons of a raccoon and an opossum.

Years later, when Samuel Chubb became a member of the staff of the American Museum and one of the outstanding comparative anatomists in the world, he went to great lengths to achieve realism and accuracy in his mounts. He was at the racetrack as often as a jockey. He took thousands of photographs and made thousands of sketches of horses in all positions. Once he dangled from a precarious rope arrangement so he could photograph the running motions of a horse from overhead. He spent hours at zoos and farms, always studying. He invented a scaffold from which all parts of a skeleton could be suspended and adjusted to get the exact position he wanted. The rig made it possible to reposition the animal countless times until it was in a perfect pose.

Chubb was in no hurry with his skeletons. Accuracy was his aim. He scorned the bug rooms because he thought the Dermestes might destroy a vital ligament, and he disliked the chemicals because they might injure a bone. Chubb macerated bones in a tub of 100-degree water for two or three weeks, and he thought it no inconvenience to sleep in the lab in order to check the bones frequently.

Chubb's mounted skeletons of a man reaching up to calm a rearing horse have become so well known they could well serve as a symbol of the American Museum of Natural History.

Along with human skeletons, the great dinosaur skeletons are among the most popular museum exhibits. These monsters that stare down at you from ceiling heights are imposing, but they are there for more than your amazement.

The more man finds out about the past, the more

he can understand the present, and, to some extent, speculate on the future. Bones from millions of years ago reveal the story of life on earth at that time, including facts about the climate and vegetation.

One hundred and twenty million years ago in the part of our continent we now call Utah, the climate was hot and moist. We know the land was covered with tall palmlike trees and giant ferns. Most of the area was dotted with swamps and lakes where the clumsy Brontosaurus wallowed, using the water to support its thirty-ton body.

An encounter between two dinosaurs might have gone this way: the Brontosaurus, leaving the water only when necessary, lumbered out on dry land one day to

Bits and pieces of a dinosaur skeleton must be fitted together like a giant jigsaw puzzle.

deposit her clutch of eggs in the warm sand. She had finished her chore and was heading for the safety of the pond when one of the monster carnivores—the meat-eaters—thundered along on his two hind legs. He was searching for a meal. Allosaurus, the meat-eater, was only half as long as Brontosaurus' sixty feet, but he was fitted for fighting with a powerful jaw full of razor-sharp teeth, and a long muscular tail that he used for balance. His dwarfed front legs looked ridiculous for his bulk, but their three great claws served as his meat hooks.

An observer of the scene would probably have described a thunderous battle between the two reptiles. Allosaurus lunged for Brontosaurus, but was knocked back by the whiplike tail of the plant-eater. He leaped again, crunching his jaws around the slender neck of the other, and both dinosaurs rolled over into the mud, their huge hulks sinking into the muck of the swamp. Both animals were trapped, to stay in their fighting position for millions of years until they were discovered by an expedition from a museum.

The first recorded discovery of ancient animal bones were those found by a twelve-year-old girl, Mary Anning, in England in 1811. Her father sold to tourists shells collected along the southern coast of England, and Mary helped him. One day she was looking for shells along a rocky shore when she found the petrified skeleton of a strange animal. Scientists were called to study the discovery, and they named the animal Ichthyosaur. It was a fishlike reptile similar in shape to present-day sharks.

Sometimes farmers plow up relics in their fields, and

amateur geologists have made extraordinary finds as they pursue their hobby. But generally the people who bring back bones and facts are trained scientists who know what they are looking for and where to look.

Before an expedition can go out it has to find financial backing. A museum has business expenses to worry about along with the research, and often it is harder to dig up money at home than it is to dig up bones in the field. But once the funds are available, plans are made to transport a crew of geologists, photographers, cooks, and helpers to the site.

The dig, which has been found by studying geological maps to locate rocky areas of the type known to contain fossils, may be difficult to reach. It may call for long treks on foot, climbs up steep cliffs, or bumpy rides over barren, blistering deserts. Or it may be as convenient to reach as the edge of town or a local riverbed.

After camp is set up, a detailed search of the terrain begins. Binoculars are used to scan cliffs; picks are used to dig out suspected rock; shovels are wielded to remove tons of sand and dirt. When a piece of bone is sighted, the exciting work begins, but not with large and fast equipment. Now the men resort to trowels, small chisels, and whisk brooms. Protection of the bone is their first concern.

It is a tedious job to remove the rock containing the skeleton. When the bones are exposed to the air they are immediately protected with a coat of shellac, and often with a layer of shellacked rice paper or shellacked cheesecloth. Then the entire section of rock to be moved is wrapped in burlap and covered with plaster, so it is protected the same way a broken leg is protected. These plaster casts are wrapped in more burlap and packed for shipping.

When the bones arrive at the museum they are sent to the paleontology lab. This lab looks, at first glance, like an industrial arts shop in a school except for the saber-toothed cat skull on the workbench and the gigantic jaw of *Tyrannosaurus rex* filling a tabletop. The hind leg of a Brontosaurus leans heavily against a cupboard. A drill press, glue pots, saws, and chisels are neatly arranged as in any shop.

Storage cupboards line the room, and when you open them you know that you are not in a wood shop. It is an ancient-parts department with rows of skulls, parts of leg bones, boxes of tiny rocklike particles recognizable only to an expert as bits of teeth and not gravel. One shelf may hold a dozen saber-toothed cat skulls waiting to be sold or traded to other museums. Many of them are not original fossil bones, but the casts of a real skull made very much like Henry Ward's fossil casts.

The dig may have produced hundreds of bones now waiting to be freed from the matrix, which is the rock in which the fossil is imbedded. The preparators begin the long task of chipping away the plaster and excess rock with tiny chisels, dentists' drills, and dental picks, working with great care and patience. As each piece is removed it is measured, sketched, and described for the records. When pieces are missing, the preparators fashion new ones from clay and plaster.

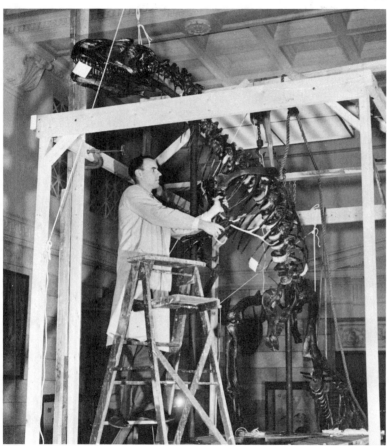

*The last step in mounting a dinosaur skeleton is the build-
ing of a temporary scaffold. The bones are supported by
metal bars placed as inconspicuously as possible.*

Like the mounting of the elephant, the building of
a dinosaur skeleton takes months and months. The final
stage is the building of a huge scaffold from which the
parts of the skeleton are suspended and welded together.

Steel rod supports are put in place as inconspicuously as possible.

Paleontologists do not spend all their time on digs or in mounting dinosaur bones. They often teach at a university; they conduct research projects on the material they have collected, and they publish papers describing their work. They have frequent requests from schools and other museums to identify parts of fossil animals. They make casts of very good or rare examples of fossils. The dinosaur eggs found by Roy Chapman Andrews in the Gobi Desert can be seen in almost every museum in the country because exact copies were cast and sold.

Much of a paleontologist's time is spent in detective work. Bits of information pieced together give clues. The long sharp teeth of one animal tell the scientist he was a meat-eater; the grinding molars of another prove that he ate leaves or grain; the bone structure of the legs and feet tell how the animal walked, ran, defended himself, and held his food. We know who his enemies were when, by luck, the bones of two fighting animals are found as they died, often with the large tooth scars of the attacker on the bones of the other. Sometimes the bones of smaller animals are found inside the skeleton of a larger animal, indicating that the larger animal may have eaten the smaller one.

Occasionally conjecture or a theory is confirmed by an event more recent. Two Canadian geologists working for a petroleum company in Peru found dramatic proof of the way hundreds of animals died in tar pits millions of years ago: they found hundreds of birds trapped in a modern tar pit only a mile from fossil tar pits.

The dinosaur expert must know mineralogy as well as anatomy, because there are times when only the expert's eye, like a human magnifying lens, can pick up things others miss. In sifting through fine gravel, only an expert could distinguish bits of bone from rock, or pieces of ancient mammal teeth from bone.

The paleontologist is also a craftsman. He uses liquid latex to reconstruct the brain of an ancient animal. He fills the holes in a skull (the nostrils, eyes, etc.) with clay or wax and, when it is watertight, fills the inside of the skull with the liquid latex. This hardens into a rubber that can be pulled out, leaving an exact replica of the brain of the animal. By measuring the volume of water held by the brain cavity, the capacity of the brain is measured. Most of the prehistoric animals had very small brains.

The men and women in the osteology and paleontology labs are explorers, carpenters, dentists, painters, and packaging experts, as well as scientists. They must train themselves to see everything, overlook nothing. Skeletons are fascinating, and the people who prepare them, study them, and exhibit them work with a sense of great accomplishment and excitement.

visitors. People like to see the strange and wonderful things that exist outside their own boundaries of life. Just as people flocked to see the bogus Onondaga giant, people today will stand in line to see a sideshow.

Museum staff members, aware of the trait of curiosity in people, try to provide more than entertainment for the public. Museums are sugar-coated schools. They dispense education with such originality and ease that there are no other institutions with as high a rate of voluntary attendance. For example, over 200 million people a year visit museums in the United States and Canada alone.

Exhibits of the quality that attracts so many people take hours of planning. The curator of a department calls a staff meeting to decide how the principles of bird flight will be illustrated, for example. One man suggests a chart; another thinks a series of miniature dioramas will be clearer. They talk over ideas. Is there room available for a life-size habitat group? How much money is available? What craftsmen will be needed—taxidermists, background painters, flower makers? In many museums all these crafts will be found in the talents of one man. In large museums a staff of specialists is available. They also decide if any items should be purchased from commercial supply houses, or if there are any animals and artifacts in storage that can be renovated for use again.

They may make a trip to the taxidermist's storeroom. Opening the door to this room is as eerie as going into a haunted house. The room is stacked from floor to ceiling with a variety of animals any zoo would have been proud to own when they were alive. A draft of air catches the outstretched wings of a noble bald eagle, and, for a moment, it seems as though it will take flight. An unborn polar bear, small enough to be held in a man's hand, nestles on a shelf next to a papier-mâché model waiting to be fitted with the pelt of a bobcat. A moose head donated by a local hunter is crammed next to a shelf full of mounted ducks wearing plastic bags to keep them clean.

The curator may decide he can use the bald eagle for his exhibit on flight, and he lists this along with other specifications to submit to the director of the museum. With the director's OK, the designer takes over. Using all the skills and resources of a theatrical designer, he studies the traffic pattern of the hall, the height and floor area available, and the variations in lighting and color.

Next time you stop to look at an exhibit, take a minute to notice the background. Color affects the mood of a room and an exhibit. A collection of cold-blooded animals is more effective, for example, against a background of cool greens and blues, and warm-blooded animals are best displayed with background colors of yellow, orange, and brown.

The invention of the light bulb did as much for museum exhibition as did progress in taxidermy. Lighting is used on the stage to emphasize or detract, and it is used similarly in museum cases. A grouping of timber wolves shown in the barren snow regions is more effec-

The background painter and taxidermists work together like stage-set designers to produce a habitat group.

tive in dim, shadowy light than it would be in the glare of overhead lighting. Rattlers in the desert look at home in a case lighted to resemble the hot noon sun.

The American Museum of Natural History uses spotlights for dramatic effect in a room devoted to the natives of the Amazon River rain forests. The room is dark. The raucous call of parrots and the drip of rain on slick leaves almost convinces the visitor that he is really in the jungle, although he knows the sound effects are on tape. As you turn the corner you meet one of the natives posed with his blowgun raised to kill a monkey. He is standing in a spotlight on an island in the room with no glass separating him from you. Lighting is an inexpensive way to bring drama to museum exhibition.

The trend is toward simplicity. In the early years of museums, when they were little more than attics, everything was exhibited together. That gave way to elaborate dioramas. Sometimes these groups were such exact replicas of nature that whole areas of soil would be transplanted, with all the plant life, directly from the woods to the museum to be copied exactly. The artists took delight in hiding tiny birds under leaves or placing insects barely visible on bark for the careful visitor to find.

But studies have shown that museum visitors seldom read all the labels and go quickly by exhibits that have too much in them to be seen easily. They would miss the birds and hidden insects even if they were there. So designers are aiming at less complex groups, taking advantage of the techniques of sound effects, lighting, and animation. Labels are planned to pack as much information as possible into a readable, easily understood small paragraph.

Before the actual work begins on a large diorama, a scale model is built because it is easier and less expensive to juggle and change models than it is to change a mounted exhibit.

A realistic habitat group results from the mating of art and science, which is what the Greek philosophers regarded as the true purpose of a museum. These groups allow people to see nature, but curators are wondering what can be done to show more of it. They would like to show, for example, a tropical rainstorm, a bird song, or the freshness of spring in the Rockies.

The scientific artists who take over after the scientists have outlined the exhibit are working on such problems. These are the men and women who can take a ball of wax, a lump of clay, plaster, and paint, and turn them into an image of nature.

Scientific Artists 7

ARTIFICIAL flowers have been made for centuries. The Egyptians used stained shavings from the horns of animals. The Romans made flowers from gold and silver, and the Chinese excelled in making delicate blossoms from rice paper. Intricate flowers have been formed from the pith of bamboo by the Japanese for hundreds of years.

South American Indians turned feathers into flowers, and the North American Indians cut petals from buckskin and decorated them with quills and beads. South Sea island natives built sprays of flowers from seashells. Today the artificial flower business is a multimillion-dollar industry supplying milliners, department-store window decorators, interior decorators, and homemakers.

Museum artists have much higher standards than people who make hats because their flowers must last longer and be more lifelike in texture and color.

If you were about to build an exhibit you would consider three methods of flower-making, depending upon the time and equipment you had and the amount of money you could spend, as well as where the flowers were to be used. If the flowers were to be seen in direct light at close range, you would choose plastic or wax flowers because they are most nearly like the real thing. But if you needed hundreds or thousands of leaves for a large tree in the background of a habitat group, you could use cotton and wax flowers, or paper flowers, which are quickly and inexpensively made.

The first step is research. The preparator studies live and preserved plants, color pictures, and notes in the reference library. Specimens brought into the lab from field trips must be cataloged, sketched or photographed, and tagged. The tag is made of linen and labeled in indelible ink so it can be put into the jar of preservative with the plant. The tag carries the plant's scientific and common names and the date and place in which it was found.

The next step is making the mold. If you were to take a carrot and press it into a box of firm sand, the carrot would leave an impression when it was removed. If you filled in that impression with another substance, modeling clay for example, you would have a duplicate carrot. The impression is the mold, the clay carrot is the cast.

If you laid a carrot in sand so that half of it was in the sand and half was out, and poured plaster over the part out of the sand, you would be making a mold. When that plaster dried you could lift it off and have a plaster impression of your carrot. If you made a mold of both halves of the carrot and clamped them together, you would have a hollow plaster mold. Then when you poured more plaster, or wax, or liquid rubber into that hollow carrot, you would have an exact reproduction of the original carrot.

That is how molds are made of each part of a flower: the petals, stem, calyx, and leaves. Wax is poured into the mold and allowed to harden. When the flower parts are removed, any rough edges are trimmed with a scissors.

Plastic is used in the same kind of mold in a method called limping. A sheet of thin plastic is allowed to go limp in a solution of acetone and water. The limp plastic is placed in the mold and worked into the veins and contours with cotton soaked in acetone. The top is put on the mold and pressed firmly for about five minutes until the acetone evaporates and the plastic is set. Rough edges are trimmed with scissors.

Large commercial firms use a vacuum-forming system, with large sheets of plastic forced into molds by a vacuum. The equipment is too expensive for the average museum, but it is the ideal way to make thousands of leaves in a hurry.

Paper leaves and petals require no mold, and they are often used to cover branches of trees in large exhibits. Heavy Japanese vellum, thin onionskin, tough brown wrapping paper, and crepe paper are all used. The shape of many leaves is cut with scissors at one time from a stack of paper, and the veins are marked with a blunt instrument. The leaves are dipped in melted wax and fine wire stems are glued to the back. Stamens and pistils are made from sewing thread or bristles dipped in hot wax.

The final coloring of the flowers makes the difference between the delicate replicas seen in museums and harshly colored, obviously artificial flowers. The artist refers to a color atlas of more than seven thousand shades keyed by letters and numbers by which he can match colors precisely with the original plant. He uses an airbrush to blow the colors on in thin coats for a translucent finish, and adds markings with a brush and oil paints. Worm holes are burned into leaves with a hot wire.

No matter what technique is used, no matter what the quality of the materials, no matter how skillfully the technique is carried out, the plants may lack realism if the preparator is unfamiliar with the natural plant. The best preparators go out of the lab on collecting trips. Only in the wet, steamy jungle of the upper Amazon can a person see how the plants there blend with the surroundings, how their color changes in a shaft of sunlight or in the afternoon shadows. Such observation is what brings life to museum exhibits.

Preparators are ever on the lookout for better ways to reproduce nature. Over two hundred years ago a German lab technician accidentally discovered a method of freeze-drying that has since been used commercially to prepare foods and in the medical field to preserve pharmaceuticals, blood plasma, and other tissues. The technician had placed a specimen in a vacuum chamber and left it overnight. The heating failed and the temperature in the lab dropped to below freezing. The next morning he found the specimen almost in its original form. It wasn't until the late 1950's that the Smithsonian Institution in Washington, D.C. began to develop the process for exhibition work. Freeze-drying is an absolutely accurate method because the animal is used just as it is brought in from the field. It is not skinned or gutted. Basically it is a process of removing the body fluids while the animal is frozen. A dead snake left in the hot sun will shrivel as it dries because it loses all the water from the body tissues. In a frozen specimen there is no shrinkage or distortion. It is an ideal procedure for delicate animals such as insects and spiders that previously had to be displayed as dry mounts or in alcohol. It has been used successfully on birds, amphibians, reptiles, fish, and small mammals. The only apparent limit to the size of the animal freeze-dried is the size of the vacuum chamber.

If a rattlesnake is needed for a diorama of the desert, the preparator takes a freshly killed snake and poses it on a bed of thick cotton batting. When the snake is in position it is covered with a layer of cotton and the technician pours liquid nitrogen over it. The cotton holds the nitrogen next to the animal as it freezes. The snake is then put into a large sealed chamber where a vacuum pump lowers the air pressure as the temperature is lowered to minus 10 degrees centigrade. It re-

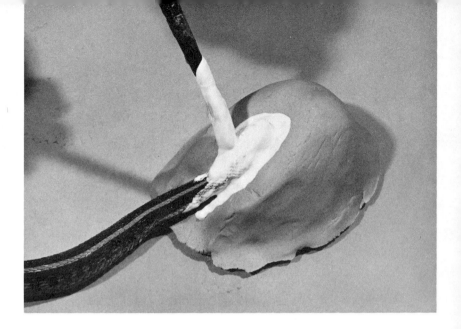

Top: A freshly killed snake is positioned with its head on clay and the first of two coats of plaster is applied— the first step in making a mold. Bottom: When the first half of the mold is dry, a thin application of water clay is painted on to act as a separator between the mold halves.

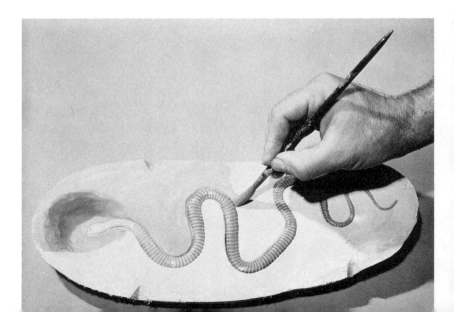

Top: The second half of the mold is made with another
application of plaster. Note the cuts in the edges of the
first mold. These are called keys and are there to assure an
accurate fit when the two halves are put together.

Bottom: The two halves of the mold are tied together; then
wedges are forced under the string to tighten the mold.
Liquid latex is poured into the mold through a clay funnel.

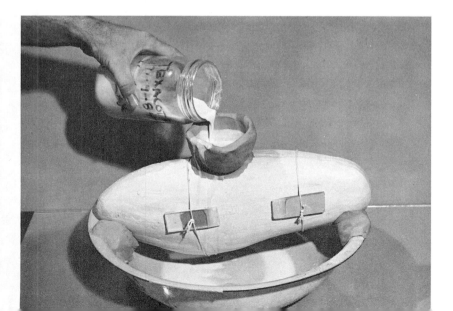

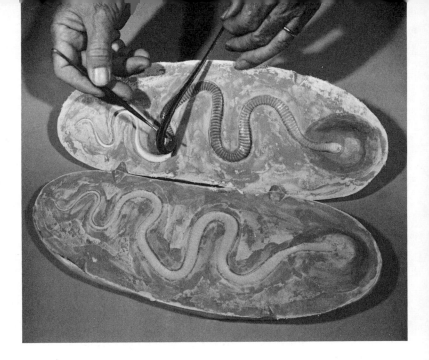

Top: The completed latex snake is removed from the mold. (This mold can be used many times.) Bottom: A latex frog and the snake will be colored with oil paints.

mains in the chamber until the ice, now in all parts of the snake's body, is converted to gas and removed by the vacuum. This may take three weeks.

When the snake is removed from the chamber it feels much like styrofoam. It has lost about 70 percent of its body weight, but, although it is very light, it has not changed in appearance at all.

Freeze-drying uses some of the techniques of taxidermy (glass eyes are usually put in and wire is used to position an animal), but it is superior to taxidermy because it eliminates gutting, skinning, and rebuilding. In the future there may be vacuum chambers large enough to hold an elephant, but then some of the excitement of the museum exhibition will be gone.

Because some animals, such as fish, reptiles, and amphibians, do not have plumage or pelts, they are not as successfully mounted by traditional taxidermy methods. Museum technicians have been experimenting with plastics, fiber glass, and rubber compounds to develop accurate methods of reproducing these animals.

Even the smallest museum with a limited budget can make authentic displays using fiber glass. It is lightweight, durable, and strong. Color can be added to the material as it is being cast, giving more depth and lifelike appearance. Very large animals can be cast in fiber glass and supported with aluminum tubing so that they can be handled by one or two men. An eight-foot porpoise cast in fiber glass weighs only twenty pounds.

Fish skins have always been difficult to mount because they dry, shrink, and crack. Even the large com-

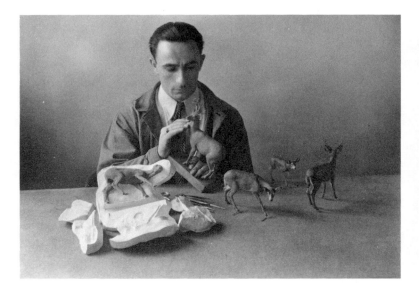

Top: An artist makes models to be used in a miniature diorama. Bottom: Finishing touches are put on a model of a small octopus for an underwater habitat group.

mercial shops that mount fishermen's prize catches use
fiber glass. They make a mold of the fish in plaster, then
line the mold with resin and glass cloth identical to that
used in making boats.

A relatively new silicone rubber compound, although still in the experimental stage, shows promise of
solving many exhibit problems. The silicone rubber can
be used to make both flexible casts and flexible molds,
valuable because there are no brittle parts that can snap
off. The rubber has been used to reproduce organs of
the human body, embryos, and tumors, as well as other
pathological specimens for medical students to study.

Silicone rubber molds are easily made. The freshly
killed animal, such as a frog, is placed in a lifelike position, propped up where necessary, and the silicone rubber is poured over it. In half an hour, when the rubber
has set, the frog is taken out, leaving a mold. Then this
empty flexible mold is coated with soap on the inside to
prevent sticking, and it is filled with a fresh batch of the
silicone rubber. After about an hour the newly made
rubber frog is taken from the mold, and it is an exact
duplicate of the dead frog. In other words, both the
mold and the cast are made from the same material, the
silicone rubber. The cast frog is completed by painting
with oils, either by airbrush or by hand.

Neoprene latex is a milky liquid also being used
to cast plants and animals in detail with maximum
strength and flexibility. The photographs on pages 78
to 80 show how the plaster mold of a freshly killed
snake is made. You can see how the liquid latex is

Top: An artist studies and sketches sargassum seaweed. He will use his firsthand information to build a realistic model of sargassum and the hundreds of tiny animals that live in it.

Bottom: On location in Bermuda, the preparator has made a mold and cast of a fish to use in a coral reef habitat group. He studies the live fish in order to paint the cast fish accurately.

poured into the mold and how, when the latex has hardened, the latex snake is removed gently from the mold. Latex is being used by taxidermists to make parts of animals that are difficult to mount. The bald heads of birds, such as condors and vultures, and the rough body forms of small animals are cast from molds made of the skinned and frozen animal. A small mouse is delicate work for a taxidermist, but it is easily skinned, the body frozen, and a mold made of plaster. Then the preparator can cast dozens, if he needs them, of the mice in latex. They can be stored for future use or they can be used immediately by mounting the skin over the latex body.

Seaweeds and other fleshy plants have been successfully cast in latex. The bark of trees is made from latex painted over large areas of the surface of the original tree. Fake trees are used because they are lightweight, do not harbor insects, and will not dry out under the exhibit lights.

Background painters are artists of great skill who blend their work with that of the other preparators. The artists go into the field whenever possible to sketch the area to be depicted. From the sketches they make small color plates in order to experiment with color before they begin the work on the life-size exhibit backgrounds. It is a tribute to these artists that visitors are seldom aware of the background because it blends so naturally with the foreground.

Realism has always been the goal of museum preparators. Now, more than ever, it is increasingly possible

Another group of biologists records animal sounds on tape to analyze for animal language patterns. Anthropologists study the relationship between magic and religion in pygmy culture. Geologists identify rock formations that lead to the discovery of oil.

The survival characteristics of the mosquito fish, known to eat two hundred mosquito larvae in an hour, are studied by a museum staff member. It might be possible to stock mosquito-breeding ponds with these fish instead of using chemical sprays.

All of these scientists work for the most important department of the museum, the research department. Research is like a tower built of blocks. Each block must be firmly in place before the next can be piled on top. Many museum researchers spend years making studies that add only one block to the tower.

Collecting specimens is part of the research. If you were to look at the first man to step off an elevator and call him the average man, you might describe *Homo sapiens* as five feet ten inches tall, bald, with brown eyes and a mustache. Of course this is no more average than the description of one snake or one skunk would be for its species. So at least thirty specimens are collected, if possible, of the same sex and age, taken from the same locality at the same time of the year. Each of these specimens is measured for every possible dimension, described, and identified with two scientific names according to the method of taxonomy devised by the botanist Carolus Linnaeus in 1753.

Taxonomy is almost a universal language for scientists. If an American ornithologist described a robin, it would not be the same as the robin known to Englishmen. But if he writes about *Turdus migratorius*, another ornithologist knows he is talking about an American robin. The exact identification is essential.

In South America there is an incurable disease known as Chagas' disease, which is caused by one species of insect. If health agencies are to find the proper method of control of this insect, they must have absolute identification of the species. Agriculturists, in their fight against pests that destroy crops, owe their knowledge of the pests and their habits to the system of identification developed by two centuries of quiet museum research. Even before scientists found out how insects breathed and what they ate, the insects were classified so that proper methods of control could be developed. Now, of course, gardeners take for granted that a spray sold in the garden store will kill their insect enemies.

A mammalogist at a museum may devote his life to the study of a small mammal, the marmoset. Even in this enlightened time some people see no sense in such a study. But this mammalogist learns how the animal breeds, what it eats, and at what temperatures it is most comfortable. He discovers that the marmoset is susceptible to human viruses. All these facts are published and become available to a cancer researcher who is looking for a small, easily handled animal that can breed in captivity and be implanted with viruses.

The study of the feeding habits of a barn swallow may have direct bearing on the ultimate decision to spray a farmer's crops. If barn swallows eat certain harmful insects, it may be better to import swallows than to spray plants grown for human consumption. Or perhaps barn swallows are themselves destroyed by eating insects that have fed on sprayed plants.

It is interesting to look in on the people who gather the collections. In an ornithology department, for example, you can see rows and rows of cupboards with many flat narrow drawers. In each drawer are rows of bird skins all carefully labeled and packed in mothballs. For every bird mounted by a taxidermist and put on display, there may be a dozen skins of that same bird in

Bird study-skins will be sorted and stored in shallow drawers with mothballs to prevent insect damage.

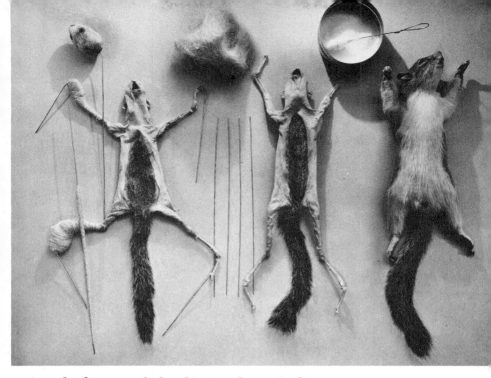

A study skin is made by skinning the squirrel in one piece through a single slit in the belly. A balsa-wood head (seen at the top left) replaces the skull. Excelsior (shown in the center) is used to stuff the body after wires, bound with thread, are placed in position to hold the legs. Arsenic (in the small container) is sprinkled on the inside of the skin as a preservative.

storage. A moderate-size museum might have one hundred thousand study skins. The large museums generally have specimens of every known bird in the world, but smaller institutions often specialize in collections of local birds.

The skins are collected from every possible source, including local parks, backyards in the city, farms, meadows, jungles, zoos, and private collections. Small birds are generally shot "gently" (an ornithologist's term for the accuracy they try for) with a .41-caliber shotgun, (commonly called a 410) using a 12-grain shot. They try to kill quickly without injuring the feathers or skin. When the bird drops, the hunter plugs the hole with a tiny bit of cotton to prevent blood from staining the feathers.

Ideally, a bird is skinned as soon as possible after it is shot. The birds are tagged, measured accurately, and weighed, and the area in which they were found is described in detail. Then the birds are gutted and skinned, and the skins are salted to preserve them. The carcass is pickled. It will be examined later to discover what the bird had eaten. Research begins at the point of collection.

Just as ornithologists can piece together a full picture of bird life from the birds he collects and observes, and paleontologists can tell the story of the era of dinosaurs, anthropologists can fit together the puzzle of man's life on earth. It is not true that dead men tell no tales. With the help of modern equipment, dead men reveal much.

Recently two mummies at the Buffalo Museum of Science were being moved to a newly decorated room, and when the curator lifted one of the ancient bodies it seemed much heavier and more solid than the other. Because fake mummies are sometimes sold to collectors (and this one had come from a private collector), the staff suspected that the mummy might be made of wood cleverly covered with linen. They did not want to attempt to unwind, and possibly damage, the delicate linen in order to find out.

They took the mummies to the Eastman Kodak Company of Rochester, New York, where a series of X rays showed the mummy to be genuine. What had seemed as heavy and hard as wood showed in the picture as yards and yards of linen stiffened with the gluey substance used in wrapping the skeleton.

From the X rays of the teeth the museum pathologists determined that the dead Egyptian was an old man, a rare thing in a time when life expectancy was short. From other pictures they learned that the man had walked for some time with a fractured hip. One pathologist commented that he had seen that kind of break during World War II. He called it a jeep break because it was commonly found in men who rode in jeeps, knees high in an almost jackknife position, over rough terrain. There was considerable speculation about this. Under what circumstances could the Egyptian have sustained a jeep break? All this evidence was recorded, and some day it may be the clue to a missing fact about the life of the Egyptians.

Those on the research staff of a science museum are never bored. If new materials were to stop coming in tomorrow, the work would not stop. The work is really never finished. It is not hurried; it deals with things that have been on earth for millions of years, and there are still millions of unanswered questions.

Museum research is divided into two parts. In addition to the work done with the collections and in the field by the ornithologists, botanists, geologists, and other scientists, there is an area called technical research that deals with the preserving and repairing of artifacts.

Constant battles are waged by museum workers to prevent damage and deterioration from the ravages of time, fire, water, light, heat, dust, humidity, atmospheric gases, fungi, vermin, "acts of God," and human beings. Even a glass bottle apparently safely placed in an exhibit case begins to lose its color or show fine cracks from the heat of the lights or from changes in the humidity. The fur on mounted animals dries and drops out or becomes brittle. Ancient clay pottery shatters when carelessly dropped.

Even as the staff works to protect the existing collection, they must do what they can to restore the original collection and stop the further decay of the objects that are brought into the museum during the year. Leather may be dry, wood rotten, textiles soiled and moth-eaten, metals rusted, and pottery cracked.

To carry personal belongings as they traveled, the Plains Indians used a large piece of buffalo hide called a parfleche, that was folded over from four sides, like an envelope. When one of these comes into a museum it is likely to be old, dirty, and stiff. The parfleche is made from rawhide, which is untanned animal skin. Tanned skin is leather.

Both rawhide and leather can be restored with light applications of warm mineral oil or vaseline. Leather that is dirty can be cleaned with soap and water scraped off with a sharp blade, as a man shaves the lather from his face. The Indians cleaned tanned skins by rubbing them with sand and then with pipe clay. Then the skin was

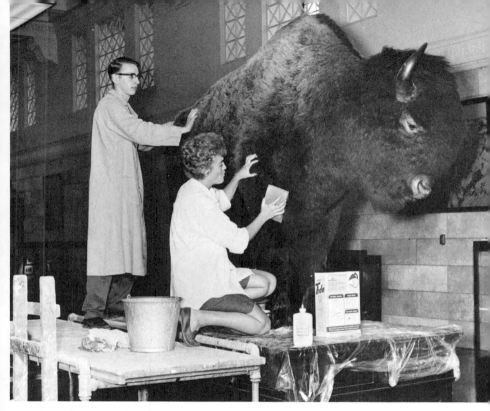

Two college students, working part time at a museum, clean the shaggy coat of a bison. They are part of a team of restorers.

shaken out and rubbed with a smooth stone. Museum workers have found that they can do the same thing by rubbing the dirty skin with white cornmeal, or fuller's earth, or artgum. When the object is clean, it is placed in a plastic bag until it is used for exhibition.

Insects are easily removed by extermination and moth balls placed in the storage cabinets prevent further damage.

Because hair is a very durable substance, it is easily cleaned with shampoo no matter how dirty or stiff it may be. Scalps or shrunken heads are carefully washed, with special care taken to keep water from the skin, and then are dried with a towel or hung to dry with the hide part on top to keep moisture from running into the skin.

Fur is cleaned with hardwood sawdust mixed with dry-cleaner's solvent rubbed into the pelt. When it is shaken and brushed out, the fur looks like new. Until they are used for exhibition, furs are put in cold storage lying flat or around cardboard tubes, where they are safe from insects and from excessive heat and moisture.

Feathers are more delicate to work with. They can be carefully washed by being shaken briskly through a shallow pan of warm soapy water. A toothbrush is some-times used to gently scrub badly soiled spots. After the feathers are dry, they are steamed to restore them further.

Porcupine quills, bone, and ivory can be washed in soap and water. They are often protected with a coat of transparent plastic sprayed on lightly.

The wood in ancient objects is sometimes so pul-verized that it is treated with a wax and resin mixture or a synthetic polyvinyl called Alvar. Wood attacked by worms is impregnated with DDT or other liquid insecti-cides. Since the Middle Ages, specialists have repaired wood with casein glue, and it is still considered one of the best adhesives for that purpose.

Baskets usually have many years' accumulation of dirt in them. They can be washed with a moist sponge and dried slowly away from direct heat. Then they are filled with sandbags to help them keep their shape as they dry. For a while technicians tried treating baskets with a coating of paraffin or wax, thinking that would protect them. But it only hastened deterioration, causing cracking and breaking, because the wax prevented the basket fibers from taking moisture from the air.

Metals, rocks, pottery, and other inorganic materials cause fewer problems. They don't deteriorate as easily, and they don't supply food for insects. Metals can be cleaned with steel wool and weak acid. Pottery can be cleaned with a 5 percent solution of hydrochloric acid. Technicians are careful to determine what materials they are working on. If they were to use the acid solution on limestone, for example, the stone would be destroyed because hydrochloric acid dissolves limestone.

Specialists in humidity control are consulted before the building of special storerooms and exhibit cases for papers and textiles that deteriorate from prolonged exposure to dry air. Libraries and art galleries, however, find this is a greater problem than science museums do.

The artifacts collected by a museum are usually irreplaceable, and the restorers' main goal is to respect the original maker and return the objects as nearly as possible to their original state.

The research departments of a natural science museum are located in the three-fourths of the building never seen by the public. Some university museums have no exhibits at all, but only great storage areas and laboratories. Research is the only reason for these museums to exist, and it is one of the important reasons for the existence of any museum.

Recording and Guarding Acquisitions 9

ONE day a man called on the curator of a small museum to donate a shrunken human head his son had sent to him from South America. He was anxious to have it out of the house because he believed it carried a curse on the family of the owner. The curator was delighted to add the head to his scanty collection.

Museums acquire objects in this manner frequently; not, of course, from superstitious people only, but from people who want to donate collections or single items they think are of value. Small boys bring toads and birds' nests. A housewife may bring in a small box holding a beetle that, when identified, turns out, much to her embarrassment, to be a cockroach. Or a collector of Indian pottery may will his collection to a local museum.

Items are added to collections through expeditions and by research teams. There is an international animal exchange through which museums and commercial supply houses can locate unusual specimens.

A commercial supply house looks like a run-of-the-mill office or small factory building until you enter the

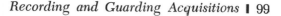

Commercial supply houses are modern, efficient factories turning out unusual products. The female technician is mounting a tarantula.

front door. There the similarity ends. The stinging odor of formaldehyde mingles with the spicy smell of plastic glue. Exhibit cases flanking the receptionist's desk offer samples of the company's wares, such as skeletons, plastic-embedded embryos, and gaudy crystals.

A typical supply house catalog is the size of a big city telephone directory, with almost as many entries. Anyone can buy a hand magnifying glass for $1.50 or a microscope for $1,500, a 150-gallon saltwater aquarium,

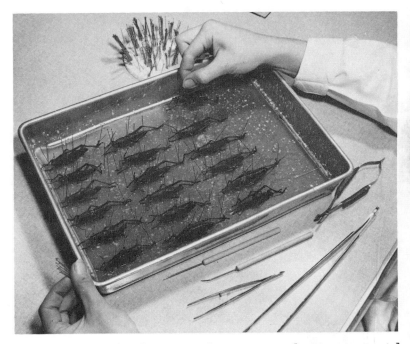

A tray of large grasshoppers is being mounted at a commercial supply house. They will be sold to schools or to museums for study.

or a cockroach. You can order a ten-cent plastic box or a $200 exhibit case. You can buy a horse skeleton for $800 or a microscope slide of a flea for eighty cents. They will supply you with a tapeworm, fireflies, or a human skeleton. They fill orders for individuals, schools, and clubs as well as museums.

Frog farms, worm farms, zoos, anticruelty societies, and amateur collectors are some of the places from which supply houses get their "merchandise." In addition, "want lists" are issued in bulletins to interested collectors. A man on the West Coast, for example, who probably knows more about the ants of California than anyone else, even though he had no more than a grade-school education, supplies commercial firms with ants for microscope slides and ant farms.

Free-lance artists are often commissioned to make special exhibits. An exhibit of microscopic pond life, enlarged about 250 diameters, was built by Edwin Reiber of Webster, New York, who developed his own formula for the plastic used in the models. This large, round exhibit, showing about fifty kinds of microscopic life, can be seen in many museums in the United States. There are studios that specialize in miniature animal models, and others that tan hides to be used by museum taxidermists.

A recent survey of one hundred museums showed that 85 percent of them purchase, at one time or another, items from commercial supply houses or from free-lance artists.

Four different categories of objects are received at museums:

1. Objects for study: things sent from other institutions or individuals for identification or research.
2. Objects as gifts to the museum or purchases for the museum's permanent collection.
3. Objects on loan for extended periods. A family sometimes allows a museum to display a collection for many years without actually giving it to the museum.

DEPARTMENTAL ACCESSION FILE

REGISTRAR ACC. NO._____

Name_____

Description_____

_____

_____

Gift_____Purchase_____Exchange_____Museum Expedition_____

Locality _____

Collector_____When Collected_____

Remarks_____

_____

Dept. Catalog Nos._____

A typical museum acquisition, or accession, card.

4. Loans for special or short-term exhibits.

Items leaving a museum are also in four groups:

1. Things sent out on loan for exhibition.
2. Objects sent to another institution for study or identification.
3. Items for trade.
4. Items for sale.

Each item, from a fragment of pottery to a book on fish, that goes in or out of the museum must be kept track of and accounted for, and that is the job of the registrar. She (it is often a woman) is also responsible for arranging for the packing, shipping, storage, and insurance coverage of all items. She is not necessarily a person with a science background.

Whatever comes into the museum, even if it is to

be there for a very short time, is given an identifying number. A card is filled out telling where the item came from, the date of entry, a short description, a record of its condition, the purpose (study, gift, etc.), the price or value for the insurance records, and the department in the museum in which it will be displayed or stored.

Then each item is given an accession number, which tells at a glance when the item arrived at the museum. This number is put on the item and on the record cards.

Accession tags tied to the feet of the bird study-skins carry the identification and the acquisition dates. They will remain as long as the birds are at the museum.

A box full of arrowheads arriving in 1968 might be the twenty-fifth shipment of the year, so it would be given the number 6825, the first two numbers indicating the year and the last two showing what shipment in that year. The number is used for all correspondence regarding the item and on all insurance and shipping notices. The number is extended for each item in the shipment. The whole box of arrowheads has the general number, 6825, and each individual arrowhead is numbered 6825.1, 6825.2, and so on.

A sketch or photograph accompanies the information whenever possible. Each item has a tag fastened to it, marked with India ink. Bones are marked with indelible ink and shellacked. Skins are tagged with linen tags tied to the feet with nylon thread. Specimens kept in alcohol are labeled on the outside of the jar, and, as an extra precaution, a linen tag is put into the jar.

The registrar also keeps disposal records. When an object can no longer be repaired it is thrown away. One disposal record listed a "god-stick," used in religious ceremonies of an ancient culture, that had been destroyed because it was infested with beetles.

Museum personnel have become expert in protecting their collections against dirt, changing temperatures, and light, but they are always looking for new ways to protect collections from people. Vandalism and robbery have added another dimension to museum work.

For no apparent reason people have written names with lipstick on dinosaurs, carved their initials in expensive display cases, and tried to pry open glass cases containing ancient coins. Children have stuck wads of gum into the fur of mounted animals not behind glass and added their own decorations to ceremonial masks.

Professional thieves, in one of America's most publicized robberies, took the Star of India, a valuable gem, from the American Museum of Natural History. They used hidden cameras to record a detailed plan of the building, and they used two-way radios to communicate during their escape. When they were caught, police found minutely detailed plans and rooftop photographs the thieves intended to use in the robberies of two other museums.

The amateur thief who follows no predictable plan, and who may take something on sudden impulse, poses a greater threat to museums than professional thieves. Precautions of all kinds are taken. Small objects are fastened to a base, and alarms are fastened to large movable objects. Closed circuit television, electronic low capacitor wiring around buildings to detect intruders at night, communications systems to summon help, and regular routine inspections by guards are commonly used.

But electronic systems can be tampered with or fail to operate, and guards can be overcome. A system of protection that is almost foolproof is the use of well-trained dogs. These animals patrol the still, dark museum corridors at night, attacking anyone other than the guard on duty with them.

One night an art class stayed later than usual at a museum, and the instructor left the room to get supplies on the opposite side of the building. The class waited and waited, and when he didn't return they went looking for him. They found him pinned to the wall by a growling German shepherd doing his duty for the museum.

King, the German shepherd watchdog that patrols the halls of the Buffalo Museum of Science, inspecting a mummy that is just arriving.

The Great Ones 10

Gone are the days of expeditions that ransacked an area to bring back everything possible to the hungry, empty museums. A new era has begun, a slower, more methodical, more selective era of collecting. It is a time of deliberate selection, of filling out collections and balancing what a museum has. Museums today cooperate more in equalizing their acquisitions and in financing expeditions.

In the early years of museums, collections were built up from curiosities sent to them from various places by the Army and Navy and other government sources.

Lewis and Clark returned from the Northwest with great quantities of Indian artifacts and strange animals.

In 1842 the Wilkes expedition returned from five years spent in the "great Southern ocean," and brought back to the Smithsonian 10,000 species of plants, 5,000 invertebrates, and 1,000 vertebrate animals.

After the Civil War, when Darwin's work spurred the study of fossils, collectors were sent into South Dakota by the Land Office with the help of a $100 grant from the Smithsonian.

In 1870 Yale sent its first expedition out to collect for the Peabody Museum of Natural History.

The 1870's yielded great numbers of animals as Ward and his men went on expeditions.

The American Museum of Natural History sent its first group into Indian Territory in 1888 to collect bison for a large habitat group. The expedition was:

> ... successful beyond expectation, as in addition to the object of the journey, the Museum acquired 325 specimens of birds and mammals, fully equalling in value the cost of the expedition.

By the end of the century large expeditions were in full swing. Wealthy men were persuaded to give great sums to back collectors going into unexplored lands. No story of museums would be complete without mention of some of the great exhibits resulting from these trips, and the amazing men who were responsible for them.

Admiral Robert E. Peary, of the United States Navy, went into the frozen Arctic many times, once to claim the discovery of the North Pole on April 6, 1909. On one of his early trips Admiral Peary noticed that the Eskimos had knives and harpoon tips made of iron, although there had been no trading in those remote regions. After many years of secrecy the Eskimos revealed the source of their iron to Admiral Peary because he had been kind to them and shown himself worthy of their trust. One day they took him by dogsled along the northern shore of Melville Bay in Greenland to the site of three immense iron meteorites that stuck out of the ice, from which the

Eskimos had been chipping bits of nickel-iron for their tools. The smallest of these meteorites was a one-thousand-pound mound that the Eskimos named "Dog" because of its shape. The second was "Woman," a fifty-five-hundred-pound shape resembling a woman hunched over sewing. The third was almost unbelievable. It was called Ahnighito or "The Tent," and Peary estimated it weighed ninety tons. However, the museum found it weighed about thirty-eight tons. The Eskimo legend said that an Innuit woman and her dog and tent were thrown out of heaven by Tonarsuk, the Spirit of Evil, and landed as stone in the ice.

Twice, after his first look at the meteorites, Peary tried to get to the iron mountains. But twice his party was forced back by heavy storms and shifting ice. Finally, in 1895, he returned on the steamer "Kite" outfitted with heavy jacks, tackles, and pulleys. They pushed through a narrow ice-jammed estuary for a mile and a half. Then they dragged jacks and cables to the meteorites. "Dog" was hoisted onto a sledge and dragged, by man and dog power, to the water's edge. "Woman" was put on a cake of ice forty feet long and seven feet thick and towed to the ship. But just as the ship's tackles were fastened to the meteorite the ice raft split. For a few terrible minutes Peary thought his prize was gone, but the lines held. The expedition groups and the Eskimos returned for Ahnighito, but the two ten-ton screw-jacks crumpled without budging the mound of iron from its ice bed. That 1895 trip triumphantly returned with "Dog" and "Woman," but without Ahnighito.

The next year Peary returned to Greenland with determination and a larger ship, the 307-ton "Hope." Peary's log tells us that "the first thing to be done was to tear the heavenly visitor from its frozen bed of centuries . . ." They used heavier jacks this time, but the work went slowly in the fierce cold. While they worked, a pack of ice drove into the beach, threatening to crush the ship. To save themselves they were forced to abandon the meteorite and go home, but they were only temporarily defeated.

In 1897 Peary was back with the same ship, but this time it had been reinforced with stronger planks, heavier rails, and more powerful jacks. And this time they were successful.

Today all three meteorites are in the Hayden Planetarium at the American Museum in New York where physicists, chemists, and astronomers can study them for clues to the mysteries of space. Meteorites are the only objects to come from beyond the earth's atmosphere, and scientists can learn much from them.

Roy Chapman Andrews' problems were the opposite of Peary's. Far from fighting ice and sub-zero temperatures, Andrews' expedition battled drought and blasting sandstorms in the Gobi Desert. In 1922 the Central Asiatic Expedition headed for the center of Outer Mongolia, the first expedition to that area to use motor vehicles successfully. There were no roads, no maps, and no reliably reported landmarks. They operated as if they were captains of ships, setting their course by stars and the compass.

One day the expedition spotted in the distance a "fantastic place, a vast pink bowl cut out of the plain by the knives of wind and frost and rain." They named it the Flaming Cliffs, because it seemed to leap like flames into the sun, and it turned out to hold an unbelievably rich deposit of dinosaur skeletons. They theorized that such a rich concentration of reptiles might have occurred at the breeding season.

This was where the famous dinosaur eggs were first seen. Like reptiles of today, the dinosaurs apparently laid their eggs in shallow holes covered by a layer of sand light enough to admit air and deep enough to keep them warm. Sometimes a windstorm heaped sand on the clutch of eggs, burying them for millions of years. Of the twenty-five eggs found, some had been exposed by erosion, some were enclosed in rock with just an identifiable end sticking out, and one nest was in sandstone so soft that it was excavated with a whisk broom.

Andrews had no difficulty removing the eggs or packing the many dinosaur skeletons. His problems were personal—the survival of his companions and himself. In the desert, temperatures drop drastically at night. This was discomfort enough, but added to it was the extreme discomfort of sleeping with poisonous snakes. The vipers crawled into tents, sleeping bags, boots, and clothing at night to find warmth. Everyone in camp got so jumpy worrying about the snakes that anyone stepping on a coil of rope screamed for help and brought men running with axes. But they did survive, and they returned safely with their valuable collection.

Carl Akeley's career moved forward quickly after his early triumph with Jumbo. In 1907 he prepared his first beautiful grouping—the fighting elephants—at the Field Museum in Chicago.

And, though he is most famous for his taxidermy, Akeley's love of perfection extended to other fields. On expeditions he observed and sketched and photographed, but he was unhappy with the stilted pictures and the limited range available. He invented the panoramic motion picture camera which opened up wide views of nature. The cameras were used by newsreel cameramen at the front during World War I.

While Akeley was working at the Field Museum, contractors were consulted about repairing one of the museum's buildings. They were asking a prohibitive amount of money, and Akeley was called upon because he could usually be counted on for problem-solving ideas. At the time Akeley was using a handmade atomizer to squirt liquid plaster under the skin of an elephant manikin. He suggested that perhaps a liquid cement could be sprayed in much the same way, using compressed air to force it out of a nozzle. So Akeley invented the cement gun. It was used in the building of the Panama Canal, on the roofs of mines, on buildings, irrigation ditches, tunnels, reservoirs, and swimming pools.

One of the things in which he took greatest pride was his sculpture, because it expressed his love and respect for nature, and for African nature in particular. He created and cast in bronze the life-size figures of

African warriors, of lions, and other African animals. They are in the Akeley Memorial Hall of African Mammals at the American Museum of Natural History.

Akeley conducted dozens of expeditions and had many exciting experiences. He was almost crushed by an injured bull elephant. He was attacked and almost killed by a leopard, but he killed the leopard with his bare hands.

Of all the animals Akeley studied, the gorillas intrigued him most. He knew the great apes as gentle animals who never attacked unless repeatedly provoked, and he planned to exhibit a typical family group showing their gentleness.

Carl Akeley's camp, in the heart of gorilla country on Mt. Mikeno in The Congo, was the scene of much activity far into the evening. The day's kill had to be skinned and preserved, and the skeletons (hanging on the crossbar) had to be cleaned. Mr. Akeley is standing between two of the movie cameras he invented.

Akeley's famous mountain gorilla as it appears in the finished habitat group in African Hall. The background is an exact copy of a spot chosen by Akeley as the most beautiful place in Africa. It is now, through his efforts, a restricted preserve for gorillas.

Akeley did not hurry into the jungle, shoot a dozen gorillas, skin them, and head for home. He lived in gorilla country for months and months taking pictures, making sketches, models, plaster casts of all the plants, and making notes on all the sounds and smells of the country as well as his own feelings about it. He shot only the specimens he needed for his group. The sacrificed animals were more than trophies to stand in public. They added to the bulk of knowledge as their skeletons were studied, measured, and compared. Their teeth were examined along with the contents of their stomachs to determine food consumption. All parts of the animals were examined.

Akeley shot his first gorilla in the mountainous district near Lake Kivu in the Belgian Congo (now The Congo), after a grueling day's climb up a steep slope in jungle so dense the expedition members had to cut their way through. Across a deep ravine one of the native boys noticed movement in the brush. It was a gorilla, but too far away to shoot. Laboriously they descended the slope, crossed the chasm, and climbed the other steep cliff until they were just under the crest of the ridge.

There was nothing between Akeley and the rocks below but a tree four inches in diameter. Suddenly a roar broke the silence, followed by a violent rush. Akeley raised his .475 rifle and fired. He reported that he hardly knew what happened in the next few seconds. The four-hundred-pound ape crashed through the thick vegetation, just missing Akeley's head. It was stopped by the small tree, and that alone saved the gorilla from hurtling to the rocks below.

The carcass was hauled back to camp where it was carefully skinned. Plaster casts, or death masks, were made of the gorilla's face, hands, and feet. The skin was cured and packed for protection against insects, and the skeleton was cleaned. The men worked far into the night by the light of gasoline lanterns.

The next day Akeley and his men went out again. Once more he shot a gorilla, and this one, too, hurtled past him but fell into the canyon. The natives wanted to return to camp, but Akeley would not think of letting a magnificent animal die for no reason. He climbed into the canyon, and by swinging and scrambling on vegetation he managed to get to the narrow ledge where the gorilla had landed. This time the animal couldn't be carried back to camp. Akeley worked on the cramped, dangerous ledge, skinning and skeletonizing his gorilla. Then he persuaded the natives to climb down and carry out the parts.

Carl Akeley tells of stalking giraffes to try to find one more than sixteen feet tall. He watched the animals grazing on treetops. Then he climbed the tree to measure how high the giraffe's head had reached. When the giraffes were collected, they were skinned through a single slit on the belly, and the leg skin was stripped off in the round like a stocking so there would be no seam showing on the legs. All of Carl Akeley's expeditions made adventure stories more exciting than fiction.

Working Together 11

DURING all the years that Carl Akeley was developing his methods of taxidermy, he had one great dream, and, finally, in 1909, while he was convalescing from a run-in with an old bull elephant in Africa, he made his plans to fulfill the dream: a great hall, at the American Museum of Natural History, containing thirty-six groups of African animals in their natural surroundings. His hope was:

> African Hall will tell the story of jungle peace; a story that is sincere and faithful to the African beasts as I have known them, and it will, I hope, tell that story so convincingly that the traditions of jungle horrors and impenetrable forests may be obliterated.

Akeley predicted that someday his exhibit, and others like it, would be the only source of study of African wildlife, as the animals gradually vanished through wanton hunting and encroaching civilization.

The dream took its first step toward reality in September, 1914, when Akeley's plans for it were approved

117

by the board of trustees of the museum. The first large section of the hall was opened officially in 1926, and the completed hall was dedicated on May 19, 1936, Carl Akeley's birthday, and ten years after his death. The years between 1914 and 1936 were spent in fund raising, the organizing of expeditions, collecting, the making of accessories (the wax plants and foliage), and the preparation of the animals.

The completed African Hall looks so peaceful that visitors seldom think of the mosquitos, the heat in the jungles, the freezing cold in the mountains, the flat tires, running out of gas in African mud, and the hauling of supplies overland by foot for months by twenty people. And that is as Carl Akeley would want it. To him all the inconveniences were minor irritations overshadowed by the greater goal.

The magnificent African Hall is the prime example of how expeditions make great exhibits, and of how many people from all departments of a natural history museum work together to achieve a goal.

Carl Akeley knew that the type of hall he envisioned might not be completed during his lifetime, and he knew that its completion depended upon a team of people trained to carry out his ideas. He hired trained specialists—collectors, taxidermists, artists, anatomists, and accessory men. He chose each man for his energy, common sense, technical or artistic ability, and, most of all, for his eagerness to do the job.

Akeley planned a complete survey of the African continent as the first step in the hall's preparation, so

Akeley's African Hall is dominated by the magnificent elephants Akeley mounted. The exhibits on the main floor and around the balcony represent all parts of Africa so perfectly that they seem to have been lifted out of the wild.

that the hall would give viewers a comprehensive idea of the topography of Africa.

The director in charge of the hall (at first it was Akeley and later it was James L. Clark) decided what groups of animals would be used, selected the locations in Africa to be depicted, studied the life histories of the animals, and directed the field work. Then a force of men from the museum, including a background painter, sculptor-taxidermists, photographers, and accessory men, met the director in Africa.

When enough material had been collected for two groups, the force of workers returned to the New York museum, and began preparations while the feel of Africa was fresh in their minds. While that first group was busy with taxidermy and related tasks, a second group of men went to Africa, where the director had chosen two more sites and two more groups of animals.

Before any part of the exhibit was built, all of the habitat groups were made in miniature on a scale of two inches to the foot. The animals were modeled, the backgrounds painted, and all the accessories were made to scale. This miniature hall was the model for the thirty-five men in the museum laboratory—including tanners, modelers, and wax workers—who worked on the hall when production was at its peak. An additional ten or fifteen mechanics were employed to build the cases and assemble the exhibits.

Each case was constructed so that it is sealed against dust and vermin, and the expansion and contraction of air occurs through tubes of fine filtering material. Electricians installed banks of lights on the inside of the cases, and these are serviced from a catwalk over the exhibits.

When materials began arriving at the museum from Africa, the registrar was busy, with his staff, recording everything.

The taxidermy, of course, was one of the most demanding and time-consuming of the jobs. But the accessory men were also working long hours. By actual record, it took six men working full time for one year to make the plants for the gorilla group, one of thirty-six groups. They had to make fifty thousand leaves. Wild celery, which gorillas eat, was made with crepe paper and wax.

The blossoms, similar to Queen Anne's lace, were each made by hand. They were cut from onion skin, wired, and coated with wax before painting. The large vines common in gorilla country were made by drawing various sizes of cotton string through hot wax. Some of the original vines from Africa were used, but they had dried and had to be restored by being soaked first in hot water, then in a preserving solution, after which they were drained and dried.

Before the background painters began their work, the accessory men installed some of the leaves and branches around the back edge of the exhibit. This was done so the painters could blend the background into the foliage without a break.

After the painting, the carpenters built a base for the animals. Lumber sections were made on swivel, roller-bearing casters so that the base would move easily. The lumber framework was covered with iron wire mesh reinforced with sisal dipped in plaster.

Then dress rehearsals were held. The gorillas were the actors. The animals and the plants were put into position, lights were tested for best effects, and often the animals were moved.

Finally, when all the animals were in place and all the plants were planted, the last operation took place. A mixture of cement and sifted ashes was applied to the plaster surface of the ground not already covered by plants, and earth was worked into the plaster. Twigs, dry leaves, or moss were added here and there for a natural effect.

The cost of reproducing the habitat—that is the background and the accessories—is 40 to 50 percent of the total cost of building an exhibit.

African Hall gives the viewer a chance to step into Africa, to see the animals resting or feeding, to see the rolling hills, the flat plains, the dense vegetation, the desert wastes. It gives the viewer who is aware of such things a chance to see what results from men and women in a museum—from the director to the storeroom clerks—working together to present a facsimile of part of the natural world we might otherwise never see.

The reticulated giraffes, shown in the water-hole group in the African Hall, were collected by Akeley along the Guaso Nyiro River in Africa. It is difficult to tell, in this realistic exhibit, where the background begins, because it blends so well with the three-dimensional foreground.

Maybe You Belong In a Science Museum

12

Roy Chapman Andrews, who found the dinosaur eggs, never wanted to do anything but work in a museum. He said, "I couldn't help it. I was born that way." Andrews, like Admiral Peary and Carl Akeley, taught himself taxidermy, and he paid for his education by mounting birds. At the close of his senior year in college Andrews went to see the director of the American Museum and asked for a job, any job.

"I'm not asking for a position. I just want to *work* here. You have to have someone to clean the floors. Couldn't I do that?"

"But," said the director, "a man with a college education doesn't want to clean floors."

"No," said Mr. Andrews, "not just any floors. But museum floors are different. I'll clean them and love it if you'll let me."

The director was perceptive enough to know that the young man he was interviewing had the makings of a real museum man.

What kind of person is a museum man? Some museum workers will smile and answer that question with, "Oh, oddballs, square pegs for round holes." But you have only to watch these people in their labs and talk to them about their work to know that what they flippantly call "odd" is really a deep dedication to an unusual career.

Museum personnel comprise a rare breed whose vocation is also a hobby. A geologist likes nothing better than to spend his summer vacation chipping trilobites from a shale creek ledge. A herpetologist admiring his neighbor's garden cannot keep from lifting a rock to see what tiny reptiles hide beneath it. An ornithologist is always an ornithologist, keeping his ears tuned to bird-calls in the city or country, keeping his eyes alert for a flash of plumage wherever he is. Taxidermists probably do not mount skunks in their kitchens, but they may be addicted to bird watching or stargazing. Having found some of the secrets of the natural world, museum people seem always to have their minds tuned for new discoveries.

Museums do not attract thousands of new employees every year as do department stores and advertising agencies. The jobs offered go to the person who asks "What are the rewards?" instead of "What is the salary?" Museum salaries are notoriously low, but are improving every year. The rewards, the fringe benefits of doing a job that is just right for you, are high.

Dr. Alexander Ruthven of the University of Michigan wrote:

A museum man is a professional zoologist, botanist, geologist, archeologist, businessman, teacher, editor, taxidermist, or some other kind of specialist, working in a museum and having a knowledge of gathering, preserving, demonstrating, and otherwise using the data which should be saved.

In other words, all museum people in all departments work toward one goal.

The administrative department is headed by the director of the museum who, like the president of a large company, organizes and directs all museum functions. Working with him are a purchasing agent, a public rela-

Vertebrate paleontology laboratory staff members study the fossil bones of an ancient turtle as they try to learn more about past life on earth.

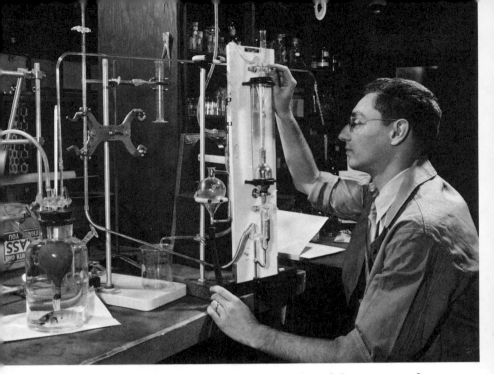

A biologist in a museum aquatic biology laboratory studies the respiration of a fish. Knowing how much oxygen and carbon dioxide are exchanged by aquatic plants and animals is a step toward combating the decline of fishes in our lakes.

tions department, bookkeepers, accountants, secretaries, and a registrar.

The scientific staff consists of the curators of each department and their assistants. These are the men and women who conduct research, lecture, and write their findings for scientific papers.

The technical branch of museum work includes the taxidermists, artists, modelers, photographers, restorers, and all the people who actually produce an exhibit.

The custodial and protective staff are the men and women who keep the museum polished, repaired, and protected. Even a museum janitor must be different from those in other buildings. A museum janitor has to know specimens from litter. He has to know how to move cases without disturbing their contents, how to pack bones, dust dinosaurs, fumigate skins, vacuum totem poles, rescue snakes, and discourage rambunctious boys.

The education departments are growing in importance in museums because they are responsible for taking the museum to the public and bringing the public to the museum. A curator is in charge of the education department, and under him are the docents, or guides, who are usually trained teachers with rich backgrounds in one or more of the sciences. They take schoolchildren on tours of the exhibit halls and conduct Saturday and after-school classes in dozens of subjects from astronomy to zoology. They supervise craft shops and help young people make their own displays. For some junior department workers, the job is a foot in the door to a position in another museum department. But most find their ideal job in the challenge of opening the doors of science to children.

The library and visual aid department is often part of the education curator's jurisdiction. Loans of films, miniature dioramas, and artifacts are made to schools and individual museum members.

The trailside museums and satellite museums are two fields particularly in need of young people in search of a fascinating career. The National Park Service sponsors a series of small museums, called trailside museums,

Guides in the junior education departments have the pleasure of introducing the wonders of nature to city children.

in the national parks. Most of these are one- or two-man museums that provide a real training ground for the person who wants to learn all phases of museum work. He would have to be preparator, janitor, director, tour guide, librarian, and secretary. Sounds like a tall order? Perhaps, but some of the young people who are taking these jobs will be the future directors of large museums, and they will be people with ingenuity and a broad understanding of museum work.

The satellite museums are like branch libraries and branch banks. A large city museum sets up a smaller version of itself in a nearby town or suburb. No preparation work is done at the satellite because exhibits are brought from the main museum. But classes are held, tours conducted, and the exhibits are available to more people than ever before.

Because museum work is so highly specialized, a college education is usually the rule, with graduate work expected for the scientific fields. A high school student who plans to prepare for museum work should take a college preparatory course with English, math, science, history, social sciences, and a foreign language. Industrial arts and fine arts courses are helpful.

In college the student should continue with some language and art, but begin to specialize in a scientific field. There are some colleges offering courses in museology (the study of museum practices and functions) and technical courses in preparation. The oldest continuously offered museum training program is presented by the University of Iowa. Their catalog says:

> Well-trained museum taxidermists have never been plentiful. At the present time there is a real shortage of well-trained men in this field of work. Opportunities in museum work are opening for women.

And then the catalog describes some of the courses:

Museum technique—to give the student a comprehensive knowledge of modern museum work. Preparing and mounting birds, mammals, and fishes. Collecting, mounting, and exhibiting museum materials including habitat group work.

Museum accessory work—modeling relief maps and miniature villages such as are used in camouflage work. Making leaves, grasses, and flowers from natural models.

Courses in general museology, which include the keeping of museum records, the place and function of the museum today, research into the preservation of collections, and the principles of exhibit and design, are offered by more than a dozen universities. A list of current programs can be obtained by writing to the American Association of Museums, 2306 Massachusetts Avenue NW, Washington, D. C., 20008. The association not only keeps a current file of courses, but offers a placement service for museum personnel.

Many museum men feel that training in the skills and techniques can be learned in apprenticeship. The Newark Museum in Newark, New Jersey, has such an apprentice program, begun in 1925, in which the trainee works in research, cataloging, storage, repair, exhibition, library techniques, public relations, and the education department.

No one individual can possibly be expert in all parts of museum work, but students intending to enter the field should be familiar with the history, objectives, and functions of museums today. And of course they will be better qualified if they are also familiar with the techniques and crafts of exhibition work.

The formal training in museum techniques is relatively new. In preparing this book, the author interviewed people at the Smithsonian Institution, the American Museum of Natural History, the Royal Ontario Museum in Toronto, the Exhibits Museum at the University of Michigan in Ann Arbor, Michigan, the Rochester, New York museum, and the Buffalo Museum of Natural Science. All of these people had come to museums from widely different fields. A Toronto ornithologist had been an aeronautical engineer, exchanging his interest in mechanical flight for bird flight. Another preparator there had started his career as an operating-room technician in a hospital, but he found he preferred the world of animals. Many had been university and high school teachers. A few had been librarians, photographers, artists. Their reasons for moving to the museums were similar: they were looking for interesting, challenging, and unusual jobs.

How do you find out if museum work is for you?

Enroll in as many Saturday and after-school classes at a nearby museum as you can. Be active in your school science club. You might be able to help set up a school museum. Visit as many museums as you can. Develop hobbies in photography, crafts, and the out-of-doors.

Ask at your local museum if there are any part-time jobs available for students. Sometimes they hire students in the summer and on Saturdays to help at the information counter or sales desk. University museums often hire students who are majoring in science as guides for elementary school tours. All of these contacts within a museum will help you to know if museum work is that very special job for you.

The qualities most needed by museum people are curiosity, intelligence, a concern for the total goal of the museum, and a disregard for regular hours, when necessary. A museum worker is a man or woman who would never consider leaving the lab if he were at a crucial point in an experiment, or of leaving the field before the collecting was done.

If a museum holds for you the combined fascination of P. T. Barnum's ballyhoo and Aristotle's noble goals; if you can say with Roy Chapman Andrews that any job—even floor scrubbing—in a museum has more appeal than banking or nursing or any other job you can name, then you have the mark of the science museum maker.

Some museums hire young people on a part-time basis to help staff their sales desks.

For Further Reading

PERIODICALS

Museum News, American Association of Museums, Washington, D.C. It is available in museum libraries.

Curator, American Museum of Natural History, New York, N.Y. This is also available in museum libraries.

Both of these magazines are written by museum staff members, and are, therefore, somewhat technical. But they give the reader an excellent idea of the work being done in museums.

BOOKS

Akeley, Mary L. Jobe, *Carl Akeley's Africa,* Dodd, Mead & Co., New York, N.Y., 1951

Akeley, Mary L. Jobe, *Wilderness Lives Again,* Dodd, Mead & Co., New York, N.Y., 1940

Katz, Herbert and Marjorie, *Museums, U.S.A.,* Doubleday & Co., Garden City, N.Y., 1965

Schwartz, Alvin, *Museum: The story of America's treasure houses,* E. P. Dutton & Co., New York, N.Y., 1967

PAMPHLETS

Careers In Museum Work, The Institute for Research, Chicago, Ill., 1964

Museum Training Courses in the United States and Canada, American Association of Museums, Washington, D.C., 1965

Printed in U.S.A.